AWESOME
BIBLE
ACTIVITIES

COLLECTIONS 1 AND 2

Written by Vickie Save
Illustrated by Ken Save

BARBOUR
PUBLISHING, INC.
Uhrichsville, Ohio

© MCMXCVII by Barbour Publishing, Inc.

ISBN 1-55748-995-5

Published by Barbour Publishing, Inc., P.O. Box 719, Uhrichsville, Ohio 44683
http://www.barbourbooks.com

 Member of the
Evangelical Christian
Publishers Association

Printed in the United States of America.

TRAVEL THE PATH THAT MAKES A SENTENCE.

START

FOR GOD SO LOVED THE WORLD THAT HE GAVE HIS ONE AND ONLY SON, THAT WHOEVER BELIEVES IN HIM SHALL NOT PERISH BUT HAVE ETERNAL LIFE

END

1

"FOR ____ SO _____ THE
_____ THAT HE GAVE ____
ONE AND ONLY ____, THAT
WHOEVER _____ IN
___ SHALL NOT _____
BUT HAVE _____
____."

JOHN 3:16

FIND THE WORDS BELOW IN THE WORD SEARCH PUZZLE.

```
J R U A M D C I W A U I H X
M G O T P N S C S M L E I J
I O E B F T L O V E D Y M G
E D R K T B J F C V T G H K
Q L Q O S E H Q P B N I P L
E A D B E L I E V E S D M T
C H R X W B S C O G K O L Q
L W O R L D A S U D U F B W
W R Q G U H O A M V K L A J
I N B S D T Y N P W A I C Z
P K L Y V L O D U X Z F O S
Z P E R I S H B N V T E K V
H F I J G F Y X H C W B H F
P E T E R N A L T O B G Q J
D N R J G Z M E X Y N V R Z
```

ETERNAL

WORLD

SON

PERISH

GOD

HIM

LIFE

BELIEVES

HIS

LOVED

3

FIND THE WORDS TO THIS VERSE
IN THE WORDSEARCH BELOW.

" FOR ALL HAVE SINNED AND FALL
SHORT OF THE GLORY OF GOD. "

ROMANS 3:23

```
R S H U K T E E B F N M T S
C I A M A Q S H O R T V C H
G E C L P V Y R F J G Y O G
T X I G L O R Y D R F S M A
D Q P B S L K Z F V C I Z H
I M A W J B T W X E G N L U
N J D K M G O O A H L N W V
O F I B W N F O R U K E R F
W A E M J Q D N S O B D G R
H Y P B T E U W V J P L C D
O M Q Y V P F A T H E G R S
E L V A L B J C N F Z Q L T
N P H S N I B H X K S L K R
F Y A F S D O O E I A B Q T
N C Z L U Q X O U F D H G J
I G O D H D A E D K V U C P
```

5

FIND THE WORDS TO THIS VERSE
IN THE WORDSEARCH BELOW.

"... WHILE WE WERE STILL SINNERS,
CHRIST DIED FOR US."

ROMANS 5:8b

```
K C E D M T W T S F E C J V
H T C A P H V A D X P J H U
P S B J F O R F R W F Z C S
A T P G S G N U J O E L O E
G I V I T B A Y V B K R G Y
N L S X W H I L E E S Z E I
M L W G O S B N I R U D R N
Y E I B L K C Q E A M Q C B
I W A H W M P N U D X B H V
L O E Z D L N S T Y H C R J
F K G O D I O R Q M F P I Z
Q R X F S D E T H B R B S P
T L J E C Q U D L D W V T K
H Y N Z D M U K S I N E L X
```

6

USE THE CODE CHART TO MATCH THE
NUMBERS WITH LETTERS. USE THE
COLUMN GOING DOWN, FIRST, THEN
WRITE THE LETTERS IN THE BLANKS.

	1	2	3	4	5	6
1	A	F	K	P	U	Z
2	B	G	L	Q	V	
3	C	H	M	R	W	
4	D	I	N	S	X	
5	E	J	O	T	Y	

"
‾‾ ‾‾ ‾‾   ‾‾ ‾‾ ‾‾   ‾‾ ‾‾ ‾‾ ‾‾ ‾‾   ‾‾ ‾‾
12 53 34   54 32 51   35 11 22 51 44   53 12

‾‾ ‾‾ ‾‾   ‾‾ ‾‾   ‾‾ ‾‾ ‾‾ ‾‾ ‾‾ , ‾‾ ‾‾ ‾‾
44 42 43   42 44   41 51 11 54 32 ' 21 15 54

‾‾ ‾‾ ‾‾   ‾‾ ‾‾ ‾‾ ‾‾   ‾‾ ‾‾   ‾‾ ‾‾ ‾‾
54 32 51   22 42 12 54   53 12   22 53 41

‾‾ ‾‾   ‾‾ ‾‾ ‾‾ ‾‾ ‾‾ ‾‾ ‾‾   ‾‾ ‾‾ ‾‾ ‾‾
42 44   51 54 51 34 43 11 23   23 42 12 51

‾‾ ‾‾   ‾‾ ‾‾ ‾‾ ‾‾ ‾‾ ‾‾   ‾‾ ‾‾ ‾‾ ‾‾ ‾‾
42 43   31 32 34 42 44 54   52 51 44 15 44

              "
‾‾ ‾‾ ‾‾   ‾‾ ‾‾ ‾‾ ‾‾ .
53 15 34   23 53 34 41

ROMANS 6:23   7

CONNECT-THE-DOTS

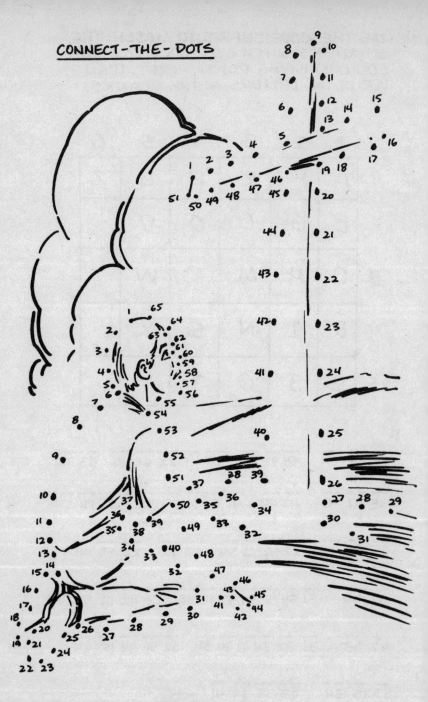

8

TRAVEL THE PATH THAT MAKES A SENTENCE.

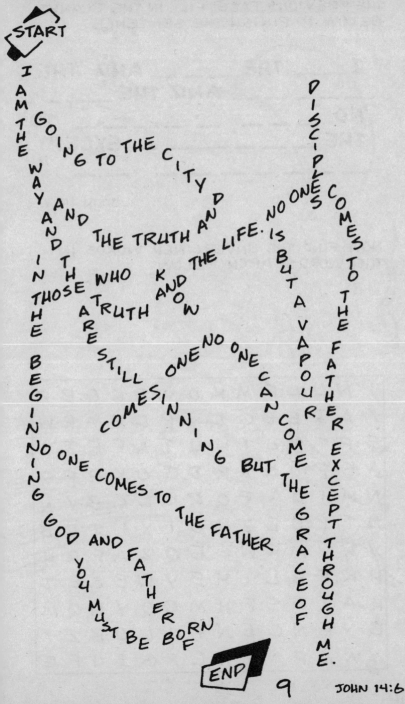

START

I AM THE WAY AND THE TRUTH AND THE LIFE. NO ONE COMES TO THE FATHER EXCEPT THROUGH ME.

END

9

JOHN 14:6

AFTER GOING THROUGH THE MAZE ON
THE PREVIOUS PAGE, FILL IN THE BLANKS
BELOW TO FINISH THE SENTENCE.

" I _ _ THE _ _ _ _ AND THE
_ _ _ _ _ AND THE _ _ _ _ .
NO _ _ _ _ _ _ _ _ _ TO
THE _ _ _ _ _ _ EXCEPT
_ _ _ _ _ _ _ _ _ _ . "

JOHN 14:6

NOW FIND THE UNDERLINED WORDS IN
THE WORD SEARCH BELOW.

```
I N U L F M K O V D K Q B R
X A J E B G T Y P L P M F W
B F T R U T H U T A F E J S
A S P L Z X R D J O K H F Q
N M I C A F O R C L C B V N
U T P O B Z U O I X I T D B
V D V M R W G E O Z A F R H
H W F E L I H B Y W B G E J
K A T S S F H M C Q Y N Q M
B Y E N C E N P H L O B Z T
Y W X F A T H E R G S U F G
```

10

USE THE CODE CHART TO MATCH THE
NUMBERS WITH LETTERS. USE THE
COLUMN GOING DOWN, FIRST, THEN
WRITE THE LETTERS IN THE BLANKS.

	1	2	3	4	5	6
1	A	F	K	P	U	Z
2	B	G	L	Q	V	
3	C	H	M	R	W	
4	D	I	N	S	X	
5	E	J	O	T	Y	

JOHN 5:24 a

"

42   54 51 23 23   55 53 15   54 32 51

54 34 15 54 32 ,   35 32 53 51 25 51 34

32 51 11 34 44   33 55   35 53 34 41

11 43 41   21 51 23 42 51 25 51 44

32 42 33   35 32 53   44 51 43 54   33 51

32 11 44   51 54 51 34 43 11 23

23 42 12 51   11 43 41   35 42 23 23   43 53 54

21 51   31 53 43 41 51 33 43 51 41 ... "

"

FINISH THE PICTURE OF JESUS.

TRAVEL THE PATH THAT MAKES A SENTENCE.

START

ROMANS 10:9

13

AFTER GOING THROUGH THE MAZE ON
THE PREVIOUS PAGE, FILL IN THE BLANKS
BELOW TO FINISH THE SENTENCE.

"IF YOU _ _ _ _ _ _ _ _
WITH YOUR _ _ _ _ _ _,
' _ _ _ _ _ _ IS _ _ _ _', AND
_ _ _ _ _ _ _ _ _ IN YOUR
_ _ _ _ _ _ THAT GOD
_ _ _ _ _ _ HIM FROM
THE _ _ _ _, YOU WILL BE
_ _ _ _ _."

ROMANS 10:9

14

FIND THE WORDS BELOW IN THE
WORDSEARCH PUZZLE.

```
I O E B F T L B C E S Y M G
E D M K T B J F C U T G H K
Q L O D S E B Q S B N I E L
E A U B A L T E V S E D A T
C H T X V B J C L G K O R Q
L W H R E D A S U I U F T W
W R Q G D H O A M V E L A J
I D B S D T Y N P W A V C 2
P K E Y V C O N F E S S E B
2 P E A L S H B N V T E K V
H L O R D F Y X H C W B H F
P E R V E L A R A I S E D J
D N R J G Z M E X Y N V R 2
```

LORD   RAISED

HEART   MOUTH

DEAD   BELIEVE

CONFESS   JESUS

SAVED   15

COLOR THE PICTURE.

JESUS IS KNOCKING AT THE DOOR OF
YOUR HEART. WHAT SHOULD YOU DO?

USE THE CODE CHART BELOW TO MATCH
THE CODES WITH LETTERS. USE THE
COLUMN GOING DOWN FIRST. THEN
WRITE THE LETTERS IN THE BLANKS
TO COMPLETE THE VERSE.

THEN YOU WILL KNOW WHAT TO DO!

	1	2	3	4	5	6	7
1	A	H	I	P	Q	X	Y
2	B	G	J	O	R	W	Z
3	C	F	K	N	S	V	
4	D	E	L	M	T	U	

"
—— —— —— —— —— —— —— !
12 42 25 42 13 11 44

—— —— —— —— —— ——
13 35 45 11 34 41

—— —— —— —— —— —— —— ——
11 45 45 12 42 41 24 24 25

—— —— ——
11 34 41

"
—— —— —— —— —— .
33 34 24 31 33

CONTINUED NEXT PAGE...

17

	1	2	3	4	5	6	7
1	A	H	I	P	Q	X	Y
2	B	G	J	O	R	W	Z
3	C	F	K	N	S	V	
4	D	E	L	M	T	U	

"
$\overline{13}\ \overline{32}\quad \overline{11}\ \overline{34}\ \overline{17}\ \overline{24}\ \overline{34}\ \overline{42}\quad \overline{12}\ \overline{42}\quad \overline{11}\ \overline{25}\ \overline{35}$

$\overline{44}\ \overline{17}\quad \overline{36}\ \overline{24}\ \overline{13}\ \overline{31}\ \overline{42}\quad \overline{11}\ \overline{34}\ \overline{41}$

$\overline{24}\ \overline{14}\ \overline{42}\ \overline{34}\ \overline{35}\quad \overline{45}\ \overline{12}\ \overline{42}\ \overline{41}\ \overline{24}\ \overline{24}\ \overline{25}$,

$\overline{13}\quad \overline{26}\ \overline{13}\ \overline{43}\ \overline{43}\quad \overline{31}\ \overline{24}\ \overline{44}\ \overline{42}\quad \overline{13}\ \overline{34}$

$\overline{11}\ \overline{34}\ \overline{41}\quad \overline{42}\ \overline{11}\ \overline{45}\quad \overline{26}\ \overline{13}\ \overline{45}\ \overline{12}$

$\overline{12}\ \overline{13}\ \overline{44}$, $\overline{11}\ \overline{34}\ \overline{41}\quad \overline{12}\ \overline{42}\quad \overline{26}\ \overline{13}\ \overline{45}\ \overline{12}$
"
$\overline{44}\ \overline{42}$.

REVELATION 3:20

18

19

DO YOU KNOW JESUS LOVES YOU? DO YOU KNOW HOW MUCH JESUS LOVES YOU? HE LOVES YOU SO MUCH THAT HE DIED TO PAY THE PRICE FOR YOUR SIN. THERE IS ONLY ONE SIN THAT GOD WILL NOT FORGIVE. THAT SIN IS NOT BELIEVING IN JESUS AND WHAT HE DID FOR YOU AND ALL OF US. WITHOUT JESUS, WITHOUT ACCEPTING THAT HE DIED FOR US, NO ONE CAN GO TO HEAVEN.

THREE DAYS AFTER JESUS DIED, HE WAS RAISED TO NEW LIFE. HE WANTS TO SHARE THAT WITH US TOO! HE WANTS TO GIVE US NEW LIFE ... ETERNAL LIFE!

DO YOU WANT TO ASK JESUS TO COME INTO YOUR HEART AND YOUR LIFE? ALL YOU NEED TO DO IS ASK HIM. YOU COULD SAY A PRAYER LIKE THIS:

DEAR JESUS,

I KNOW I AM A SINNER AND THAT YOU DIED FOR ALL MY SINS. I KNOW YOU ROSE FROM THE DEAD. JESUS, I ASK YOU NOW TO COME INTO MY HEART AND TAKE CONTROL OF MY LIFE.
THANK YOU FOR ALL YOU HAVE DONE FOR ME.
TEACH ME YOUR WAYS, JESUS, AND HELP ME TO GROW UP WITH YOU.

IN JESUS' NAME, I PRAY. AMEN.

IF YOU HAVE NEVER INVITED JESUS INTO YOUR HEART AND LIFE BUT YOU WANT TO NOW, GO TO THE NEXT PAGE AND WRITE OUT YOUR PRAYER IN YOUR OWN WORDS. JUST TELL JESUS HOW YOU REALLY FEEL.

MY VERY OWN PRAYER TO INVITE
JESUS INTO MY HEART AND LIFE.

DATE : _____

DEAR LORD JESUS ,

_____

_____

_____

_____

_____

_____

_____

_____

_____

_____

IN JESUS' NAME, AMEN.

_____
YOUR NAME

DID YOU INVITE JESUS INTO YOUR HEART?

FIND YOUR WAY TO JESUS:

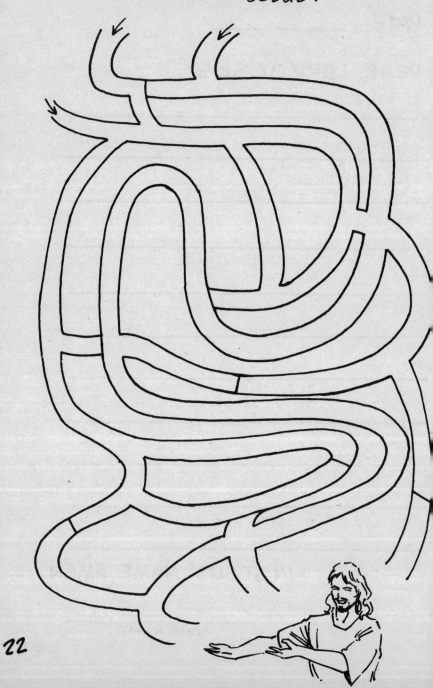

WOW! IF YOU ASKED JESUS INTO YOUR LIFE, YOU ARE NOW A CHRISTIAN! YOU ARE NOW A CHILD OF GOD!

LET'S LEARN HOW TO GET TO KNOW JESUS BETTER.

UNSCRAMBLE THE WORDS BELOW TO FIND OUT HOW TO BEGIN.

1.) TO BECOME A CHILD OF GOD, YOU HAD TO ASK JESUS INTO YOUR HEART. THIS IS CALLED _____ .
IYGNRAP

2.) PRAYING IS _____ WITH GOD.
GTINALK

3.) JUST LIKE YOU TALK WITH YOUR MOM OR DAD, GOD_____ YOU TO _____ WITH HIM.   TWNAS   KTLA

4.) IT DOES NOT STOP THERE. GOD WANTS TO TALK TO YOU! JESUS SPEAKS TO YOU THROUGH HIS _____ .
DRWO

5.) THE ONLY WAY TO REALLY KNOW JESUS IS TO_____ ABOUT_____ .
ARDE   IMH

6.) YOU READ ABOUT _____ IN THE HOLY _____ .   JSSUE
EBLIB

IN THE FOLLOWING WORDSEARCH PUZZLE,
FIND AND CIRCLE THE WORDS LISTED.

THEY CAN BE FOUND IN LINES GOING
FORWARD, BACKWARD, UP, DOWN, OR
DIAGONALLY.

```
D F C L P V Y R F H G V O G
O X S R A E H Y D R I S M A
O Q P B S L K Z F V C M Z H
R M B W J B E A T H G N L V
N J D K M N Q O A H L N W O
O F I B O N F O U K R P I
W A E Y J Q D N S N B D G C
H K N O C K U W V J A L C E
O A Q Y V P F A T P B T R S
V L E A L B D E V O L Q S T
```

LOVED   HEARS   EAT

KNOCK   VOICE   ANYONE

DOOR   HIM   STAND

24

WHAT HAVE YOU LEARNED ABOUT BEING A CHILD OF GOD?

FIND AND CIRCLE THE WORDS LISTED BELOW.

```
T X I G D O R Y D R F S M A
D Q P R S L K Z F V C I K H
I M O W J B T W X R G N L U
N W D K M G O O U H L N A V
B F I B W N G D N U R K T F
W I E M J B I B L E B D G R
H N P B T V U W V J D L C D
O V Q Y A R P A T H A G R S
H I W S L B J S U S E J L T
N T H S N I B H X K R L K R
F E F A S D O S E A I B Q T
N C Z L U Q X O U F D H G J
I G O D H D A E D K V U C P
```

PRAY	WORD	TALK
READ	JESUS	GOD
BIBLE	SAVIOUR	INVITE

25

CONNECT THE DOTS
AND FINISH THE PHRASE.

JESUS, THE ____ ____ OF JUDAH!

ACROSS

1. GOD <u>EAVG</u> US HIS ONE AND ONLY SON.

2. NOW WE CAN HAVE ETERNAL <u>FILE</u>.

3. JESUS KNOCKS AT THE DOORS OF OUR <u>TARHES</u>

4. IF WE HAVE <u>TIVDEIN</u> HIM IN, HE WILL NEVER <u>LEAVE US</u>.

DOWN

5. WE ARE NOW A CHILD OF <u>ODG</u>.

6. WE TALK TO HIM BY <u>YRANIGP</u>.

7. HE TALKS TO US THROUGH <u>SHI</u> WORD.

8. HIS WORD IS THE <u>BBEIL</u>.

<u>WORD LIST</u>

PRAYING	HEARTS
LIFE	BIBLE
GAVE	HIS
INVITED	GOD

27

SOMETIMES, IT'S NOT EASY TO READ THE
BIBLE EVERY DAY. OTHER *THINGS*
WILL TRY TO GET IN THE WAY, BUT IF YOU
REALLY WANT TO GROW AS A CHRISTIAN, IT IS
BEST TO READ IN GOD'S WORD EACH DAY.

FIND YOUR WAY TO THE BIBLE.

START

WHEN THE COUNSELOR

NOW
I
AM
GOING
PLAINLY ABOUT MY
I HAVE CHOSEN
MAKING
IT
KNOWN TO BUT WILL I WHOM, COMES
I AM
I HAVE
COMING
SEND
TO YOU TO THIS
FROM
SPIRIT THE ,FATHER THE IS ETERNAL LIFE
EACH
TO HIS TRUTH
OLD YOU
OF TRUTH WHO GOES OUT THE SPIRIT OF
THESE
FROM THE
TESTIFY WILL HE
LIGHTS OF ,FATHER
WILL SEE
ABOUT ME. NO
FOR

END

AFTER GOING THROUGH THE MAZE ON THE PREVIOUS PAGE, FILL IN THE BLANKS BELOW TO FINISH THE SENTENCE.

"WHEN THE _ _ _ _ _ _ _ _ _ COMES, _ _ _ _ _ I WILL _ _ _ _ _ TO _ _ _ FROM THE _ _ _ _ _ _ , THE _ _ _ _ _ _ OF _ _ _ _ _ WHO _ _ _ _ OUT FROM THE FATHER, HE WILL _ _ _ _ _ _ _ _ _ _ _ _ _ ME."

JOHN 15:26

31

FIND THE WORDS BELOW IN THE
WORDSEARCH PUZZLE.

```
H N P B T V M W V G D L C D
O V Q Y A O P T T O A G S S
H I W S H B J S E E E J E T
N C H W N I B H W S R L N R
F E O A S D O S E A T B D T
N C Z U U T R U T H D I G J
A G O D N D A E D K V U F P
B F I B W S G O D U R K T Y
O I E M J B E B L E B D G R
U N P B T V U L V J D L C D
T V Q Y A R P A O H A G R S
H I W S L B S P I R I T L T
N T H S N I B H X K R Y O U
```

SPIRIT   WHOM   YOU

ABOUT   TRUTH   TESTIFY

GOES   COUNSELOR   SEND

COLOR THE PICTURE

WHEN YOU BECOME A CHILD OF GOD,
WHERE DOES THE HOLY SPIRIT LIVE?

GO ON TO THE NEXT PAGE TO FIND
THE ANSWER.

	1	2	3	4	5	6	7
1	A	H	I	P	Q	X	Y
2	B	G	J	O	R	W	Z
3	C	F	K	N	S	V	
4	D	E	L	M	T	U	

"
__ __ __ __ __ __ __ __ __ __ __ __
41 24 17 24 46 34 24 45 33 34 24 26

__ __ __ __ __ __ __ __ __ __ __ __
45 12 11 45 17 24 46 25 21 24 41 17

__ __ __ __ __ __ __ __ __ __ __
13 35 11 45 42 44 14 43 42 24 32

__ __ __ __ __ __ __ __ __ __ __ __ __
45 12 42 12 24 43 17 35 14 13 25 13 45

__ __ __ __ __ __ __ __ __ __⁷
26 12 24 13 35 13 34 17 24 46

__ __ __ __ __ __ __ __ __ __ __
26 12 24 44 17 24 46 12 11 36 42

__ __ __ __ __ __ __ __ __ __ __ __ __ __ __ ?
25 42 31 42 13 36 42 41 32 25 24 44 22 24 41

34

1 CORINTHIANS 6:19

THE HOLY SPIRIT ACTUALLY COMES TO LIVE INSIDE YOU! YOUR BODY BECOMES THE TEMPLE, OR DWELLING PLACE, OF GOD'S SPIRIT.

THIS IS HARD TO UNDERSTAND BECAUSE WE CAN'T SEE HIM, BUT IT IS TRUE BECAUSE THE BIBLE SAYS IT IS SO. MANY TIMES THE HOLY SPIRIT MAKES HIS PRESENCE KNOWN. WE CAN FEEL HIM AS HE GIVES US HIS POWER AND STRENGTH TO LIVE AS GOD WANTS US TO LIVE.

CONNECT-THE-DOTS

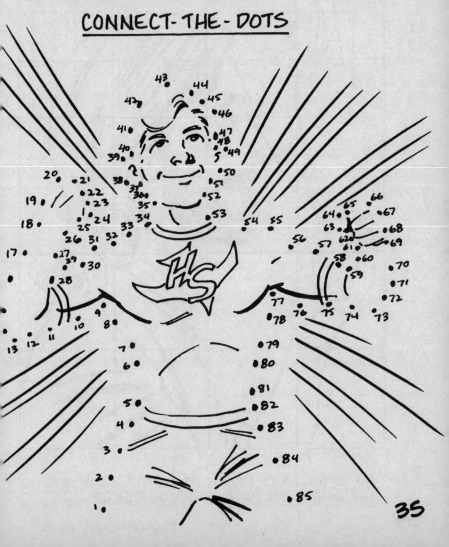

35

ONCE, OUR HUMAN SPIRITS WERE DEAD. WE WERE BORN SPIRITUALLY DEAD. JESUS GIVES US NEW LIFE IN OUR SPIRITS!

"FOR JUST AS THE FATHER RAISES THE DEAD AND GIVES THEM LIFE, EVEN SO THE SON GIVES LIFE TO WHOM HE IS PLEASED TO GIVE IT."

JOHN 5:21

GO TO THE NEXT PAGE. USING THE GRID, DRAW THE ABOVE PICTURE FOR YOURSELF.

FROM THE PREVIOUS PAGE, USE THE
GRID TO DRAW THE PICTURE FOR YOURSELF.

NOW THAT YOU ARE A CHRISTIAN, YOU MUST
LET THE HOLY SPIRIT TEACH YOU HOW TO
LIVE YOUR NEW LIFE. HOW DOES HE DO
THIS?

USE THE CODE CHART BELOW TO MATCH
THE CODES WITH LETTERS. USE THE
COLUMN GOING DOWN, FIRST, THEN WRITE
THE LETTERS IN THE BLANKS ON THE
FOLLOWING PAGE.

	1	2	3	4	5	6	7
1	A	B	C	D	E	F	G
2	H	I	J	K	L	M	N
3	O	P	Q	R	S	T	U
4	V	W	X	Y	Z		

WHAT YOU PUT INTO YOUR MIND, WHAT
YOU READ OR WATCH OR LISTEN TO, IS
WHAT WILL COME OUT OF YOU. IF YOU
PUT GOD'S WORD IN, IF YOU READ THE
BIBLE REGULARLY, GOD'S CHARACTER
WILL COME OUT OF YOU IN THE WAYS YOU
THINK, ACT AND THE CHOICES YOU MAKE.

USING THE CODE CHART FROM THE
PREVIOUS PAGE, COMPLETE THE VERSE
BELOW.

(1

—— —— —— —— —— —— —— —— —— —— ——
14 31   27 31 36   13 31 27 16 31 34 26

—— —— —— —— —— —— —— —— —— —— —— ——
11 27 44   25 31 27 17 15 34 36 31 36 21 15

—— —— —— —— —— —— —— —— —— —— —— ——
32 11 36 36 15 34 27   31 16   36 21 22 35

—— —— —— —— —— , —— —— —— —— ——
42 31 34 25 14   12 37 36   12 15

—— —— —— —— —— —— —— —— —— —— —— ——
36 34 11 27 35 16 31 34 26 15 14   12 44

—— —— —— —— —— —— —— —— —— —— ——
36 21 15   34 15 27 15 42 22 27 17

                                    ))
—— —— —— —— —— —— —— —— —— —— .
31 16   44 31 37 34   26 22 27 14

ROMANS 12:2

39

COLOR THE PICTURE

SHOOT 'EM UP COMICS

BE CAREFUL IN YOUR CHOICES!

40

TRAVEL THE PATH THAT MAKES A SENTENCE.

START

DO NOT

ANYONE WHO RECEIVES THE SPIRIT

BUT THE FRUIT OF

USE YOUR LOVE JOY PEACE

LET US

FULNESS GOODNESS KINDNESS PATIENCE

THOSE WHO WANT

NOT

BROTHER

BE

GENTLENESS

TO MAKE A

COME

WERE AND MERCY TO

LET US

ALL W

GROW WEARY

SELF-CONTROL.

NOT

WHO

AND

BECOME

THE PEACE

LED TO BE

END

41

GALATIANS 5:22-23a

AFTER GOING THROUGH THE MAZE ON
THE PREVIOUS PAGE, FILL IN THE
BLANKS BELOW TO FINISH THE VERSE.

" BUT THE _ _ _ _ _ _ OF
THE _ _ _ _ _ _ _ IS

_ _ _ _ , _ _ _ ,

_ _ _ _ _ ,

_ _ _ _ _ _ _ _ ,

_ _ _ _ _ _ _ _ _ ,

_ _ _ _ _ _ _ _ ,

_ _ _ _ _ _ _ _ _ _ ,

_ _ _ _ _ _ _ _ _

AND _ _ _ _ _ - _ _ _ _ _ _ _ _

GALATIANS 5:22-23 a

FIND THE WORDS BELOW IN THE WORDSEARCH PUZZLE.

```
P F O S P I R I T A J B D G
N A Z U E T R U T H O I G O
A I T K N L A E D K Y U F O
B T I I W S F R U I T K T D
O H E N E B E C L E B D G N
U F P D T N U L O J D L C E
A U O N N D C E D N V U F S
B L I E W S G E D U T K T S
C N E S J B E L B B E R G R
H E W S L B S P I C L T O T
N S H S N I B H A K R O O L
T S G E N T L E N E S S V S
H I W S L B P P I D T I L E
```

JOY	KINDNESS
SELF-CONTROL	SPIRIT
GENTLENESS	PATIENCE
PEACE	GOODNESS
FRUIT	LOVE
FAITHFULNESS	

THE FRUIT OF THE SPIRIT

FILL IN THE BLANKS.

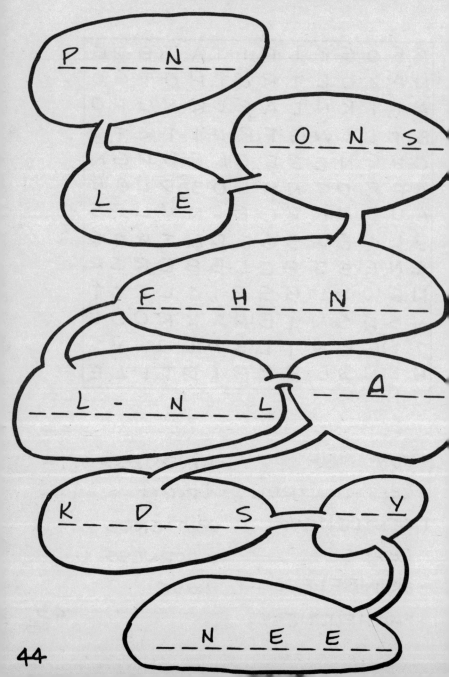

YOU ALREADY KNOW THAT WHEN YOU
BECOME A CHRISTIAN, THE HOLY SPIRIT
COMES TO LIVE IN YOU. THE HOLY SPIRIT
WILL LEAD YOU INTO GOD'S TRUTH, AND
HE WILL DO THE WORK OF PRODUCING
GOD'S CHARACTER IN YOU, IF YOU WILL
LET HIM. YOU CAN DO THAT BY CHOOSING
TO DO WHAT GOD WANTS RATHER THAN
WHAT YOU WANT. THIS IS CALLED
SURRENDERING, OR GIVING UP, TO GOD'S
WILL.

GOD'S CHARACTER IS THE FRUIT OF
THE SPIRIT.

UNSCRAMBLE THE WORDS BELOW TO
FIND GOD'S CHARACTER, THE FRUIT OF
THE SPIRIT.

OVLE   _ _ _ _

OYJ   _ _ _

PCEEA   _ _ _ _ _

TIEENCPA   _ _ _ _ _ _ _ _

DNNESKSI   _ _ _ _ _ _ _ _

OGDOSSNE   _ _ _ _ _ _ _ _

HTAIFLUNFSES

              _ _ _ _ _ _ _ _ _ _ _

TNLEEEGSSN

              _ _ _ _ _ _ _ _ _

- RTNSFLEOCLO

              _ _ _ _ - _ _ _ _ _ _ _

FIND YOUR WAY THROUGH THE
OBSTACLES, THE THINGS OF THIS WORLD,
THAT WILL TRY TO PULL YOU AWAY FROM
WHAT GOD WOULD WANT YOU TO DO.

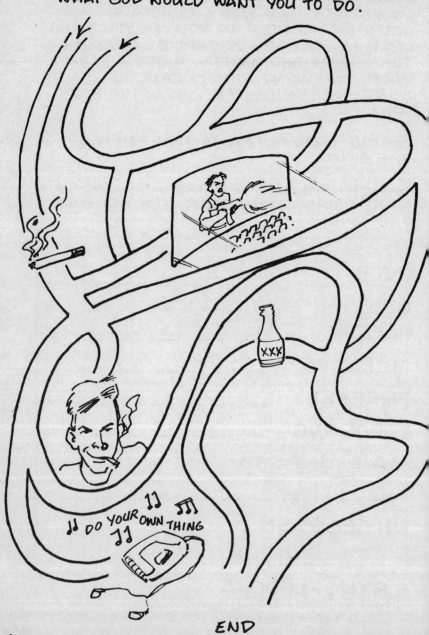

END

FINISH THE PICTURE

AS YOU START TO LIVE YOUR NEW LIFE AS GOD'S CHILD, IT IS IMPORTANT TO KNOW WHO YOUR ENEMIES ARE!

THE CHRISTIAN HAS THREE ENEMIES:
1. THE DEVIL
2. THE SINFUL NATURE (THE FLESH)
3. THE WORLD

A CHRISTIAN IN THIS WORLD IS LIKE A SOLDIER — A SOLDIER OF THE LORD. YOUR ONLY WEAPON IS THE BIBLE.

USE THE CODE CHART BELOW TO MATCH THE CODES WITH LETTERS. USE THE COLUMN GOING DOWN, FIRST, THEN WRITE THE LETTERS IN THE BLANKS.

	1	2	3	4	5	6	7
1	A	B	C	D	E	F	G
2	H	I	J	K	L	M	N
3	O	P	Q	R	S	T	U
4	V	W	X	Y	Z		

"
__ __   __ __ __ __   __ __ __ __ __ __   __ __ __ __
12 15   35 15 25 16   13 31 27 36 34 31   25 25 15 1

__ __ __   __ __ __ __ __ .   __ __ __ __
11 27 14   11 25 15 34 36   44 31 37 34

__ __ __ __ __   __ __ __   __ __ __ __ __
15 27 15 26 44   36 21 15   14 15 41 22 25

__ __ __ __ __ __   __ __ __ __ __ __
32 34 31 42 25 35   11 34 31 37 27 14

__ __ __ __   __   __ __ __ __ __ __ __
25 22 24 15   11   34 31 11 34 22 27 17

__ __ __ __   __ __ __ __ __ __ __
25 22 31 27   25 31 31 24 22 27 17

__ __ __   __ __ __ __ __ __ __
16 31 34   35 31 26 15 31 27 15

                    "
__ __   __ __ __ __ __ __ .
36 31   14 15 41 31 37 34

1 PETER 5:8

WHAT DO YOU NEED TO DO WHEN THE
DEVIL TEMPTS YOU TO SIN?

AS YOU GO THROUGH THE MAZE, COLLECT
THE LETTERS AND COMPLETE THE
STATEMENT BELOW.

_ _ _ _ _ _ _ THE DEVIL!   51

WHAT IS THE DEVIL LIKE ?

AS YOU GO THROUGH THE MAZE, COLLECT THE LETTERS AND COMPLETE THE STATEMENT BELOW.

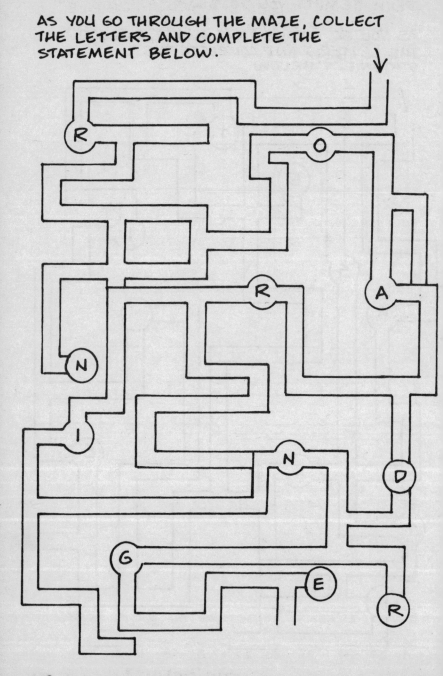

52 THE DEVIL IS LIKE A _ _ _ _ _ _ _ LION!

PSALM 119: 104-105 GIVES ANOTHER
DESCRIPTION OF GOD'S WORD, THE BIBLE.
USE THE CODE BELOW TO COMPLETE THESE
TWO VERSES. USE THE COLUMN GOING
DOWN FIRST.

	1	2	3	4	5	6	7
1	A	B	C	D	E	F	G
2	H	I	J	K	L	M	N
3	O	P	Q	R	S	T	U
4	V	W	X	Y	Z		

"___ ___ ___ ___ ___ ___ ___ ___ ___ ___ ___
22 17 11 22 27   37 27 14 15 34

___ ___ ___ ___ ___ ___ ___ ___ ___ ___ ___ ___
35 36 11 27 14 22 27 17   16 34 31 26

___ ___ ___ ___ ___ ___ ___ ___ ___ ___ ___ ___ ;
44 31 37 34   32 34 15 13 15 32 36 35

___ ___ ___ ___ ___ ___ ___ ___ ___ ___
36 21 15 34 15 16 31 34 15   22

___ ___ ___ ___ ___ ___ ___ ___ ___
21 11 36 15   15 41 15 34 44

___ ___ ___ ___ ___ ___ ___ ___ ___ .
42 34 31 27 17 32 11 36 21

___ ___ ___ ___ ___ ___ ___ ___ ___ ___ ___
44 31 37 34   42 31 34 14   22 35 11

___ ___ ___ ___ ___ ___ ___ ___ ___ ___ ___ ___
25 11 26 32   36 31   26 44 16 15 15 36

___ ___ ___ ___ ___ ___ ___ ___ ___ ___ ___ ___
11 27 14   11   25 22 17 21   36 16 31 34
                          11

___ ___ ___ ___ ___ ___ .
26 44   32 11 36 21

THE BIBLE IS A LAMP THAT LIGHTS OUR
WAY IN THE DARKNESS OF SIN AND
TEMPTATION.

USING THE GRID, DRAW THE PICTURE
BELOW ON THE NEXT PAGE.

FROM THE PREVIOUS PAGE, USE THE
GRID TO DRAW THE PICTURE FOR YOURSELF.

THE SECOND ENEMY IN OUR WALK WITH THE LORD IS OUR SINFUL NATURE, ALSO KNOWN AS THE "FLESH". THIS SINFUL NATURE OR FLESH IS A PART OF ALL OF US. WE ARE BORN WITH IT.

USE THE CODE CHART BELOW TO MATCH THE CODES WITH LETTERS. USE THE COLUMN GOING DOWN, FIRST, THEN WRITE THE LETTERS IN THE BLANKS.

	1	2	3	4	5	6	7
4			Z	Y	X	W	V
3	O	P	Q	R	S	T	U
2	N	M	L	K	J	I	H
1	A	B	C	D	E	F	G

"

36 27 15   11 13 36 35   31 16   36 27 15

35 26 21 16 37 23   21 11 36 37 34 15   11 34 15

11 21 17 15 34 ?   25 15 11 23 31 37 35 44 ?

21 31 36 35 27 11 34 26 21 17 ?   27 11 36 26 21 17 ?

23 44 26 21 17 ?   22 11 24 26 21 17   31 36 27 15 34 35

11 21 17 34 44 ?   46 31 34 35 27 26 32 26 21 17

16 11 23 35 15   17 31 14 35 ?   11 21 14

"

46 26 36 13 27 13 34 11 16 36 .

GALATIANS 5:19-21
(CHILDREN'S BIBLE)

56

FIND THE WORDS BELOW IN THE WORDSEARCH PUZZLE.

WORSHIPING	ANGRY
ACTS	JEALOUSY
SINFUL	HATING
NATURE	LYING
FLESH	SHARING

```
A I T K S L F L E S H U G O
B W I I T S F R U T T N T D
O O E N C B E C L E I A G N
U R P D A N U L O Y D T C E
A S O N N N C E L N V U F S
B H A T I N G E D U T R T S
O I E N E B E R R E B E L N
U P P D T N U L Y J D U E C
A I O N N P C E D N F U F S
B N I E S H A R I N G K T S
C G E S J B E L I E B R G R
U E W S L B S S I C L T O T
N S J E A L O U S Y R O O L
```

THE BIBLE TELLS US HOW TO FIGHT THE
DESIRES OF THE SINFUL NATURE.

USE THE CODE CHART BELOW TO MATCH
THE CODES WITH LETTERS. USE THE
COLUMN GOING DOWN, FIRST, THEN WRITE
THE LETTERS IN THE BLANKS.

	1	2	3	4	5	6	7
4			Z	Y	X	W	V
3	O	P	Q	R	S	T	U
2	N	M	L	K	J	I	H
1	A	B	C	D	E	F	G

"

36 27 31 35 15   46 27 31   12 15 23 31 21 17 36 31

13 27 34 26 35 36   25 15 35 37 35   27 11 47 15

13 34 37 13 26 16 26 15 14   36 27 15   35 26 21 16 37 23

21 11 36 37 34 15   46 26 36 27   26 36 35

32 11 35 35 26 31 21 35   11 21 14   14 15 35 26 34 15 35 .

35 26 21 13 15   46 15   23 26 47 15   12 44   36 27 15

35 32 26 34 26 36)   23 15 36   37 35 24 15 15 32

26 21   35 36 15 32   46 26 36 27   36 27 15

35 32 26 34 26 36 . "   GALATIANS 5:24-25

FIND THE WORDS BELOW IN THE WORDSEARCH PUZZLE.

```
U F P D T P C O S P R R T I A
A L O N N F O R G I V E U T H
B L I E W A N T K N L A P D K
C N E S J I F I I W S F U U I
J W S E L T E E N E B E R L E
U S H S N H S P D T N U I O J
S S G E N F S O N N D C F D N
T I W S L U L I E W S G V U
E W S G E L N E S J B E L B E
U N R I G H T E O U S N E S S
S L B S N N S H S N I B H A K
S N I B H S S G E N T L E N R
E N T L E H I W S L B P P I T
```

FORGIVE   SINS

FAITHFUL   JUST

PURIFY   CONFESS

UNRIGHTEOUSNESS

73

OUR LORD JESUS PAID THE PRICE FOR OUR SINS. HE TOOK OUR PUNISHMENT BY DYING ON THE CROSS.

USING THE GRID, DRAW THE PICTURE BELOW ON THE NEXT PAGE.

THE ONLY WAY TO HEAVEN IS THROUGH
JESUS CHRIST. HAVING JESUS IN YOUR
HEART MEANS YOU HAVE BEEN GIVEN
ETERNAL LIFE, AND YOU WILL LIVE WITH
GOD FOREVER. THIS IS GOD'S PROMISE
TO YOU!

FIND THE UNDERLINED WORDS IN THE
WORDSEARCH PUZZLE BELOW.

"I GIVE THEM ETERNAL
LIFE, AND THEY SHALL NEVER
PERISH; NO ONE CAN SNATCH
THEM OUT OF MY HAND."

```
S N E S J I F I I W S F U H
J N P E T E R N A L B R E L
U S A S N H S E D T N U I O
P Q G T N F T V N N D C F D
T S W S C U L E E W S G H T
I H H B A H E R T L E N A C
T A E H I W S L B E P I N E
L L E P N E G E F L E T D C
N L S E D T N I I O J N F O
E F S O N M L C V D N W A N
T U L E D W G S V E U J I F
E L N E B J B L S B E L T E
G P E R I S H N E S S N U S
```

FROM THE START OF YOUR CHRISTIAN L
TO THE END OF IT, YOU WILL ALWAYS STA
IN THE HAND OF THE LORD JESUS.

LIFE WILL NOT ALWAYS BE EASY, BUT
JESUS WILL GET YOU THROUGH!

FIND YOUR WAY THROUGH THE MAZ
OF LIFE.

START

END

85

IF YOU REMEMBER, WHEN YOU INVITE
JESUS CHRIST INTO YOUR LIFE, YOUR BODY
BECOMES THE TEMPLE OF GOD'S HOLY SPIR

IN OTHER WORDS, YOUR BODY BECOMES TH
"HOUSE" THAT THE HOLY SPIRIT DWELLS IN
AS YOU LIVE IN A HOUSE THAT NEEDS
CLEANING, SO DOES YOUR "BODY-HOUSE"
NEED CLEANING. THE HOLY SPIRIT WANTS
TO CLEAN UP WRONG THINKING AND
ACTIONS.

THE HOUSE WITHOUT JESUS:

COLOR THE PICTURE.

AGAIN, IT IS THE WORK OF THE HOLY SPIRIT THAT DOES THE CLEANING IN US. HE ONLY NEEDS US TO BE WILLING TO LET HIM DO THAT WORK.

GOD'S WORD GIVES US A PROMISE!

FIND THE UNDERLINED WORDS IN THE WORDSEARCH PUZZLE BELOW.

"BE **CONFIDENT** OF THIS, THAT HE WHO **BEGAN** A **GOOD** **WORK** IN YOU WILL **CARRY** IT ON TO THE **FINISH** UNTIL **JESUS** **CHRIST** COMES **AGAIN**."

PHILIPPIANS 1:6
(CHILDREN'S BIBLE)

```
P Q G T N F B V N N D C Y D
T S W S C U L E E W S R H T
I W O R K H E R G L R N A C
F A E H I W S L B A P I N C
I L E P N E G L C E N I N H
N Q G T G F T V N N A W C R
I U L C O N F I D E N T P I
S L N H O J B L S B G H F S
H P E R D S H J E S U S W T
E L N E B J B X Y B Z T L D
```

PICTURE YOURSELF AS A SOLDIER!
YOU ARE NOW A SOLDIER FOR JESUS
CHRIST, AND HE GIVES US EVERYTHING
WE NEED TO WIN THE BATTLE.

USE THE CODE CHART BELOW TO MATCH
THE CODES WITH LETTERS. USE THE
COLUMN GOING DOWN FIRST, THEN WRITE
THE LETTERS IN THE BLANKS.

	1	2	3	4	5	6
5	A	F	K	P	U	Z
4	B	G	L	Q	V	
3	C	H	M	R	W	
2	D	I	N	S	X	
1	E	J	O	T	Y	

$\overline{52}$ $\overline{22}$ $\overline{23}$ $\overline{51}$ $\overline{43}$ $\overline{43}$ $\overline{15}$, $\overline{41}$ $\overline{11}$

$\overline{24}$ $\overline{14}$ $\overline{34}$ $\overline{13}$ $\overline{23}$ $\overline{42}$ $\overline{22}$ $\overline{23}$ $\overline{14}$ $\overline{32}$ $\overline{11}$

$\overline{43}$ $\overline{13}$ $\overline{34}$ $\overline{21}$ $\overline{51}$ $\overline{23}$ $\overline{21}$ $\overline{22}$ $\overline{23}$ $\overline{32}$ $\overline{22}$ $\overline{24}$

$\overline{33}$ $\overline{22}$ $\overline{42}$ $\overline{32}$ $\overline{14}$ $\overline{15}$ $\overline{54}$ $\overline{13}$ $\overline{35}$ $\overline{11}$ $\overline{34}$

CONT'D NEXT PAGE...

CONT'D FROM PREVIOUS PAGE.

$\overline{54}$ $\overline{55}$ $\overline{14}$ $\quad$ $\overline{13}$ $\overline{23}$ $\quad$ $\overline{14}$ $\overline{32}$ $\overline{11}$ $\quad$ $\overline{52}$ $\overline{55}$ $\overline{43}$ $\overline{43}$

$\overline{51}$ $\overline{34}$ $\overline{33}$ $\overline{13}$ $\overline{34}$ $\quad$ $\overline{13}$ $\overline{52}$ $\quad$ $\overline{42}$ $\overline{13}$ $\overline{21}$

$\overline{24}$ $\overline{13}$ $\quad$ $\overline{14}$ $\overline{32}$ $\overline{51}$ $\overline{14}$ $\quad$ $\overline{15}$ $\overline{13}$ $\overline{55}$ $\quad$ $\overline{31}$ $\overline{51}$ $\overline{23}$

$\overline{14}$ $\overline{51}$ $\overline{53}$ $\overline{11}$ $\quad$ $\overline{15}$ $\overline{13}$ $\overline{55}$ $\overline{34}$ $\quad$ $\overline{24}$ $\overline{14}$ $\overline{51}$ $\overline{23}$ $\overline{21}$

$\overline{51}$ $\overline{42}$ $\overline{51}$ $\overline{22}$ $\overline{24}$ $\overline{23}$ $\overline{14}$ $\quad$ $\overline{14}$ $\overline{32}$ $\overline{11}$
,

$\overline{21}$ $\overline{11}$ $\overline{45}$ $\overline{22}$ $\overline{43}$ $\overline{24}$ $\quad$ $\overline{24}$ $\overline{31}$ $\overline{32}$ $\overline{11}$ $\overline{33}$ $\overline{11}$ $\overline{24}$."

EPHESIANS 6:10-11

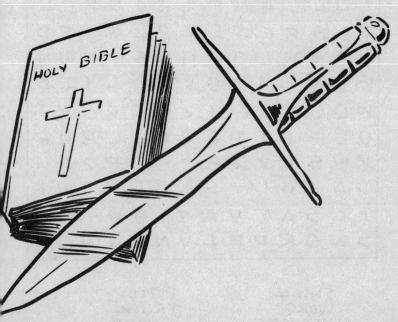

FIND THE UNDERLINED WORDS IN THE WORDSEARCH PUZZLE BELOW.

" STAND FIRM THEN, WITH THE <u>BELT</u> OF <u>TRUTH</u> BUCKLED AROUND YOUR WAIST, WITH THE <u>BREAST PLATE</u> OF RIGHTEOUSNES IN PLACE, AND WITH YOUR FEET <u>FITTED</u> WITH THE READINESS THAT COMES FROM THE <u>GOSPEL</u> OF PEACE. IN ADDITION TO ALL THIS, TAKE UP THE <u>SHIELD</u> OF FAITH, WITH WHICH YOU CAN EXTINGUISH ALL THE FLAMING ARROWS OF THE EVIL ONE. TAKE THE <u>HELMET</u> OF <u>SALVATION</u> AND THE <u>SWORD</u> OF THE SPIRIT, WHICH IS THE <u>WORD</u> OF GOD. "

EPHESIANS 6: 14-17

THIS IS THE FULL ARMOR OF GOD!

```
I U L C H N F I G O S P E L
S L B R E A S T P L A T E D
H P E R L S H H E S U T W N
E L N E M J B X I B L T L D
W Q G T E F B V N E D C Y T
O S F I T T E D B W L R H R
R W B R K H E R G L R D A U
D A E H I W S L B D P T W T
I L S A L V A T I O N I N H
S W O R D F T V N N A W C R
```

SHIELD	FITTED
WORD	TRUTH
HELMET	SWORD
BELT	GOSPEL
SALVATION	BREASTPLATE

FIND YOUR WAY THROUGH THE BATTLEFIELD OF LIFE. WATCH OUT FOR TEMPTATION AND SIN!

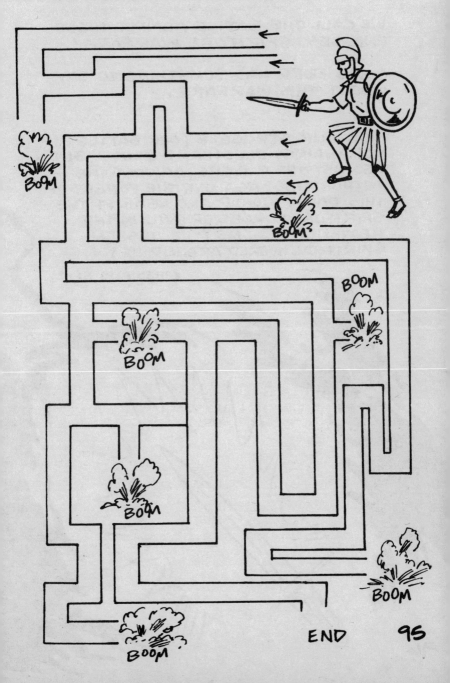

END

95

DO YOU REMEMBER OUR THREE ENEMIES,
THE *WORLD*, THE *FLESH* (OR SINFUL NATURE),
AND THE *DEVIL*?

WE CALL THE BATTLE AGAINST THESE
ENEMIES *SPIRITUAL WARFARE* !

GOD'S WORD HAS SOMETHING TO SAY
ABOUT THIS WARFARE.

" FOR OUR STRUGGLE (OUR BATTLE) IS
NOT AGAINST FLESH AND BLOOD, BUT
AGAINST THE RULERS, AGAINST THE
AUTHORITIES, AGAINST THE POWERS OF
THIS DARK WORLD AND AGAINST THE
SPIRITUAL FORCES OF EVIL IN THE
HEAVENLY REALMS (THE UNSEEN
SPIRITUAL WORLD AROUND US). "

EPHESIANS 6:12

FIND THE WORDS BELOW IN THE
WORDSEARCH.

```
      C H B F L G O
   L B R E F L E S H
    E B R L I H O E S U
S E L N T V J B X O B
  T Q G E W F B V W D C Y
D P R F L T O S D P X D
  R A U T H O R I T I E S
W D N H G V W S L B D P T W
  P L S A G V D T D N Z H
H E A V E N L Y V G J Q C R
  L N R U L E R S W L
    B R K H S N G L R
   H   W   L
```

FLESH   RULERS

EVIL   BLOOD

WORLD   HEAVENLY

STRUGGLE   AUTHORITIES

NOW IT IS TIME TO START LIVING YOUR LIFE AS A CHILD OF GOD.

THERE ARE MANY THINGS IN LIFE THAT CAN DISTRACT US, OR LEAD US AWAY, FROM JESUS.

WHAT DOES JESUS SAY WE SHOULD DO?

UNSCRAMBLE THE WORDS AND PUT THEM IN THE RIGHT PLACES IN THE VERSE BELOW.

" LET US <u>XFI</u> OUR EYES ON <u>SEUJS</u> THE <u>RATUHO</u> AND PERFECTER OF OUR <u>AFHIT</u>, WHO FOR THE <u>OYJ</u> SET <u>EBRFEO</u> HIM ENDURED THE <u>ORSCS</u> SCORNING ITS <u>MHSEA</u>, AND SAT <u>WODN</u> AT THE RIGHT <u>NDHA</u> OF THE <u>HTNROE</u> OF GOD."

HEBREWS 12:2

" LET US ____ OUR EYES ON _____, THE _____ AND PERFECTER OF OUR _____, WHO FOR THE ___ SET _____ HIM ENDURED THE _____, SCORNING ITS _____, AND SAT _____ AT THE RIGHT _____ OF THE _____ OF GOD."

98

WORDSEARCH

```
I D L J G Q P A N G E L
G J A I L I U T K P W U
A O N X H D S L A V E C
D H D S A O G E B O T R
H Z R Z D L R T I R X F
P O M N G S C T A B Q V
W T Y J U D G E M E N T
M C S J O E H R Y I F K
W O H L B Y A S T O R M
V I S I O N E F J S E V
```

JUDGEMENT

JOY

HEART

LETTERS

JAIL

WORSHIP

IDOLS

VISION

SLAVE

ANGEL

STORM

GOD

WORDSEARCH

```
B T W I E L D E R S D A J
I G J A H T N I Y N H O C
V E E T H I O P I A N Z P
H N R V P C Z F U P Y I B
G T U S H M B X G S L X Q
O I S T G R J Q S I W D C
Q L A L S T E P H E N B F
N E L D O C W P A J E M G
D P E A N T I O C H A K D
K U M E Z F S T O N I N G
J V D L U T H E L R Y K R
E M F K F I W S X N H J E
```

SEEK   ELDERS
STEPHEN   STONING
PHILIP   ANTIOCH
ETHIOPIAN   DEATH
JEWISH   GENTILE
JERUSALEM   FIND

WORDSEARCH

```
K X C S P E E C H T F S V M
A D P Q T B E L I E V E R S
P Q R B F M A R C Z K A W R
O A P C O Y I A U P V X L O
S N C E B P E N T E C O S T
T W J T S G F K J T S B G L
L I D Y S G R A C E T Y W D
E R L Y A Y O Z P R A Y E R
S O L H U I U C S G U T H Q
H Q J E L P N H I Z M X L N
H E A V E N V E C H U R C H
```

HOLY SPIRIT   BELIEVERS
HEAVEN   APOSTLE
PENTECOST   GRACE
PETER   SPEECH
ACTS   CHURCH
PRAYER   SAUL

WORDSEARCH

```
R T B L V H I I L O N S O
Q H E A L S B A I L M A D
V P F M Z A N H S H J L W
C K I T P R N Y T R U T H
M G L A E T C I L Y B H P
L P O T N B A P T I S M G
O D E G K F S T A F G Z E
V F Q W X J F Y I L M H K
E Q S A L V A T I O N C T
I T E R T W D X E J N Q V
```

SALVATION	FAITH
BAPTISM	LIFE
WAY	TEMPTATION
HEALS	ETERNAL
TRUTH	SALT
LIGHT	LOVE

WORDSEARCH

```
H W F A T H E R T E O
E Y K L R K V B S O C
M J X I U S C L X M F
L A S L A U E W N Y D
R M T K V P J G L D J
H E S T S U A O Y B E
B S G O H J H D H P S
F Z G C N E T Z I N U
Q M A R K P W M A J S
G D T R I N I T Y Q N
```

HOLY	JOHN
SON	GOSPELS
LUKE	FATHER
MATTHEW	MARK
JAMES	TRINITY
GOD	JESUS

SEARCH FOR IT

FIND THE NAMES OF THE FOUR GOSPELS BELOW.

(HINT: THE FIRST FOUR BOOKS OF THE NEW
TESTAMENT ARE CALLED THE GOSPELS.)

```
N U J R L D O E M O B K
K L A J O N T F C U M S
R M D X N L H I G D A Z
T J M A T T H E W E R J
L K I C S P A L N H K Q
E U D I A R K G O B O M
M F K X W G C J G Q E A
L A H E N P B Y A M Q R
W N T I J O H N P M Y B
F Z J T H V F C B Y P H
```

_____   _____

_____   _____

WORDSEARCH

```
B U E S T H E R T P H R Y
Q E A M R E Z E K I E L C
T P S A L M S G J Z D L H
S M L N E H E M I A H S R
F O D O Z C F L S Y B C O
I G L A R H E J I R M X N
J P X O A U A V E S O I I
S K N I M R B V W K H Q C
B N A F N O O B D Q K A L
O S I H J R N H G B V L E
I T C E P W Z P K I N G S
```

NEHEMIAH   ESTHER
ELISHA   EZRA
JOB   ISAIAH
SOLOMON   PROVERBS
PSALMS   CHRONICLES
KINGS   EZEKIEL

WORDSEARCH

```
B I M Y H Q L X T R I A L S F
G F A I T H V D N R O M O J P
R C O S G P F Q C W U C R U C
S A W A B C S H A L D T D E E
H E A R T I D A V I D N H O C
E W S E R P J K L X B V E G A
P R A I S E P I V M P G U Z I
H E Z R N J E B A E U F Q S G
E R Q E L N I T M F G T D O H
R V D U R D E N E S Y N K N E
D S J P F H Z R K X M O T G T
```

HEART   REFUGE
TRUTH   TRIALS
SINNER   SONG
PSALM   PRAISE
SHEPHERD   LORD
DAVID   FAITH

WORDSEARCH

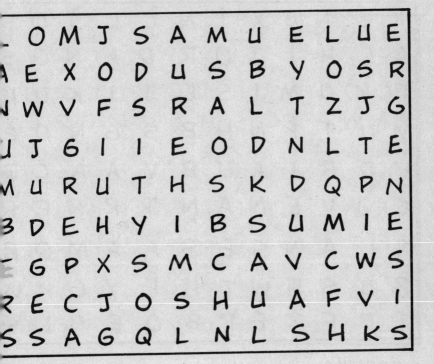

```
L O M J S A M U E L U E
A E X O D U S B Y O S R
N W V F S R A L T Z J G
U J G I I E O D N L T E
M U R U T H S K D Q P N
B D E H Y I B S U M I E
L G P X S M C A V C W S
R E C J O S H U A F V I
S S A G Q L N L S H K S
```

SAUL	EXODUS
GENESIS	JOSHUA
LEVITICUS	SAMUEL
RUTH	NUMBERS
JUDGES	MOSES

WORDSEARCH

```
K I N G X J N C L J Q R
A C H I J O R D A N O S
P R O M I S E J I K D H
M U T P N H B S G N O E
V D R I A U B V A A C B
C O V E N A N T R R F R
H L A W S E S A A M Q E
B U S H W T H F Y G K W
T D F Z E P B O E P L S
```

JOSHUA
JORDAN
SIN
COVENANT
PROMISE
STANDS

KING
LAWS
REST
HEBREWS
BUSH
PHARAOH

GOD'S PROMISE

GOD HAS GIVEN ABRAM A NEW NAME THAT MEANS FATHER OF NATIONS. HE HAS PROMISED ABRAM A SON.

CROSS OUT EVERY LETTER THAT APPEARS FOUR TIMES— WRITE THE REMAING LETTERS IN ORDER TO FIND HIS NEW NAME.

C P A D L W E S I
F Y T G I B Q G Q
W E S K Q F Q C Y
R L Y P A W Y K G
K T H C D T S D I
S F K P E T A W G
C L D M E L P F I

WHAT IS HIS NEW NAME ? _____

WORDSEARCH

```
I D S P C G A K M V U O D K S N H
O H O L Y S P I R I T D P I E K P
U D Y W O C W M X Z X B T D R J M
G T R F N X E O I J B E R W P N J
Q R B I H Y A L R T Q A B A E H S
T E L O Z A B P F D G J Z Q N P F
N E D E N G P Y K F L H N I T O D
J Q E X A W V N J U A K W L R J W
G L Y S H Q K T E M P T E D S I C
F D E V A R Z Y C W L H B C T G H
A S X K W N Q O D U N G M O B T Q
B D S E R V G M Z R V D B T R I W
S R A C J C U E Z A Q T R A U M L
E D T M N X V P L F A G E F Y L V
M T D C R E A T I O N H X S V U G
L R Y E O Z U F M Y C H K F T N I
```

ADAM
CREATION
SWORD
TREE
SERPENT
GARDEN

ANGEL
HOLY SPIRIT
EARTH
EVE
TEMPTED
EDEN

WORDSEARCH

```
I X L O B N Z U N F J A Z T U Y F
E B M Z A D O C K I M H L O R D A
P O R H B P F V X G L K Y D I G L
Y L T O A K N A W O H T Y C A N S
R A C W D B H U T C G B F M H D M
N S E M O E A X U H J W I S D O M
V F O C Q B A T T L E A P Q L Z G
C J K L X D Z B H J V R V A K N R
I H W O O R B G Q S O M S W I R I
T K D Y U M S E A W H B A K F Q E
D E G A J C O L F I A E I G L M F
S Q V L P T S N Z K P N B N Y U H
J P M A R R I E S H T X E A S R I
```

BATHSHEBA   ABSALOM
URIAH   FATHER
MARRIES   LOYAL
LORD   BATTLE
NATHAN   KING
GRIEF   ZADOCK
SOLOMON   WISDOM

WORDSEARCH

```
C I P L H O S P T S A G
Q A F A T Z F D E R W H
K E D R L G P N M I R V
Q U B M J A R G P J N I
J H S K E V C K L X J M
E T W G M B W E E P O H
R D L R P N S A F Z N H U
U C A X W U A N K Q A J
S Q A N O I N T E D T B
A D H H G Y U M H I H Y
L N E B C E L W O A A O
E T L T O A R K D P N U
M V J E V Y D X F M C Z
```

WEEP   JERUSALEM
DANGER   PALACE
ARMY   ARK
JONATHAN   TEMPLE
ANOINTED   NATHAN
JUDAH   HOUSE

FIND THE WORDS

T	M	H	Q	C	Y	S	S	R	O	A	H
B	S	F	L	N	O	V	D	T	C	T	I
W	O	G	A	L	I	L	E	E	I	X	U
J	L	T	E	H	J	R	G	A	X	D	M
N	D	G	F	A	E	N	F	O	C	F	I
U	I	K	P	S	I	V	R	H	L	S	J
M	E	D	G	L	A	T	K	Q	T	F	A
O	R	N	A	C	R	O	M	A	N	Y	I
W	U	E	B	G	X	K	O	D	Z	B	R
R	H	Q	I	L	T	B	E	P	J	N	U
J	I	S	R	A	E	L	M	H	V	W	S

ROMAN   JAIRUS
FAITH   HEALING
GALILEE   SOLDIER
BOAT   ISRAEL

FIND THE WORDS

P	S	D	O	N	L	Q	A	C	F	Z	K
G	N	P	J	E	S	U	S	T	N	M	R
O	J	G	U	L	I	C	Y	H	B	E	B
D	H	F	S	V	O	C	O	O	T	Z	A
S	O	D	L	C	A	J	P	S	D	O	P
T	M	V	R	G	N	S	L	S	Y	S	T
Q	L	A	E	A	F	Y	T	Q	P	P	I
N	V	Q	D	N	J	C	D	N	E	I	Z
C	T	R	S	S	A	V	I	O	U	R	E
F	O	W	R	H	S	T	E	C	X	I	G
J	P	D	K	Z	D	M	I	T	W	T	I

JESUS   BAPTIZE
SPIRIT   GOD
JOHN   SAVIOUR
JORDAN   DOVE

FIND THE WORDS

```
C D S A U L H L P H G
S A M U E L I E W X I
R N F A I T H K A R A
D R R P D A V I D R N
R S L I N G Q N U F T
I J A E V I M G B O K
P B E T H L E H E M L
H C J F G O L I A T H
A B A R M O U R D P G
```

SAUL	HEART
ISRAEL	GOLIATH
KING	GIANT
SAMUEL	ARMOUR
BETHLEHEM	SLING
DAVID	FAITH

CONNECT THE DOTS

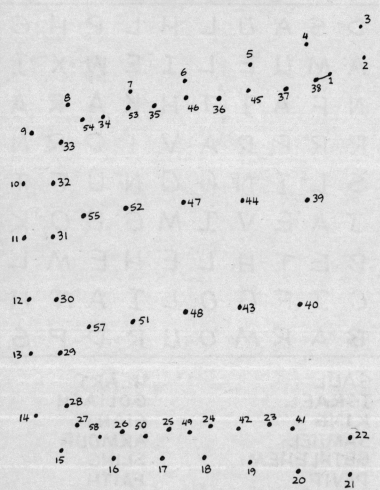

CONNECT THE DOTS

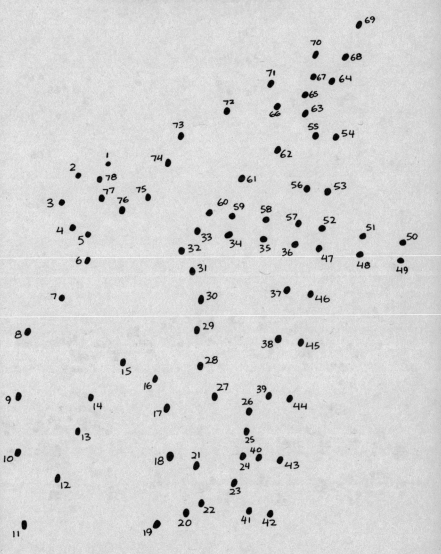

CONNECT THE DOTS

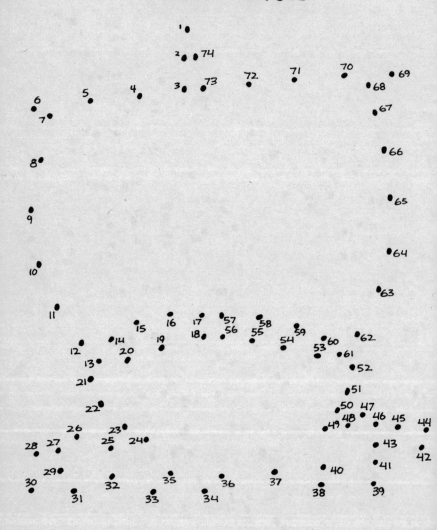

CONNECT THE DOTS

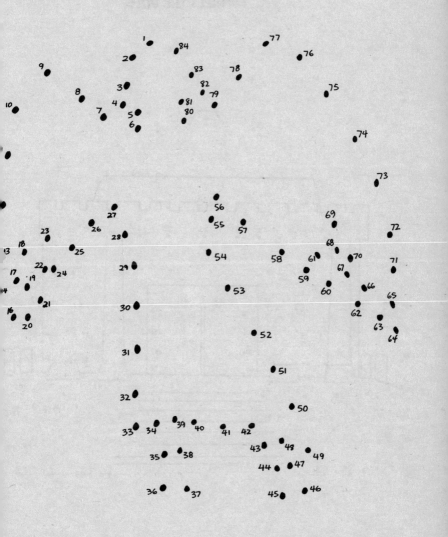

HELP BUILD THE TEMPLE
CONNECT THE DOTS

CONNECT THE DOTS

YOUNG DAVID WENT TO BATTLE AGAINST--?

UNSCRAMBLE:

HGTLIOA

__ __ __ __ __ __ __

CONNECT THE DOTS

JESUS , THE _____ OF JUDAH !

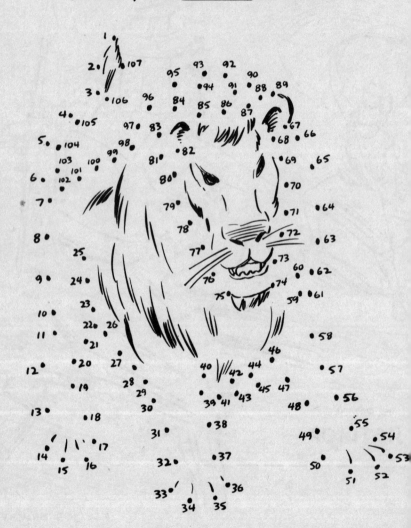

CONNECT THE DOTS
PETER WALKS ON THE WATER

CONNECT THE DOTS

JESUS HAD RIDDEN INTO JERUSALEM ON THIS ANIMAL

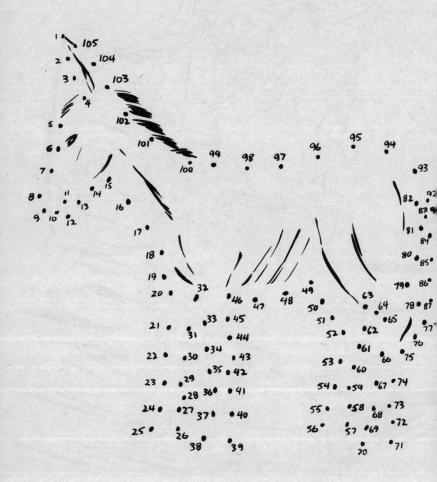

CONNECT THE DOTS

SAUL MET JESUS ON THE ROAD TO DAMASCUS.

GOD CREATED A BEAUTIFUL GARDEN FOR ADAM AND EVE TO LIVE IN. THE SERPENT TEMPTED THEM TO DISOBEY GOD. WHICH TREE DID THEY EAT FROM WHEN THEY SINNED?

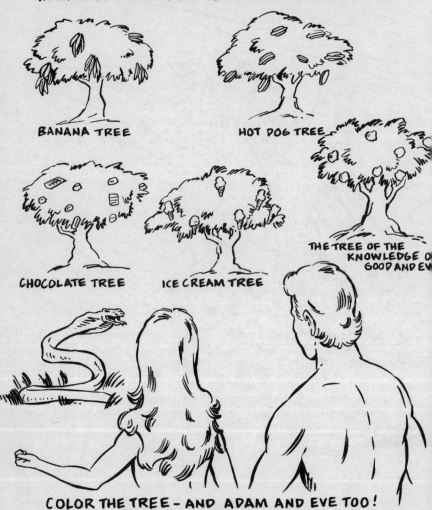

BANANA TREE

HOT DOG TREE

CHOCOLATE TREE

ICE CREAM TREE

THE TREE OF THE KNOWLEDGE O GOOD AND EV

COLOR THE TREE - AND ADAM AND EVE TOO!

SOLVE THE PUZZLE AND COLOR THE PICTURE

GOD GAVE A PROMISE TO NEVER DESTROY THE WORLD AGAIN BY WATER. WHAT SIGN DID HE GIVE OF HIS PROMISE? USE THE CIRCLED LETTERS TO FIND THE ANSWERS.

NOAH BUILT AN __ O__ .

__ __ O__ WAS THE ONLY GOOD MAN LEFT.

IT WOULD __ __ O__ FOR FORTY DAYS AND NIGHTS.

THE __ O__ __ __ __ __ CAME INTWO BY TWO.

THE O__ __ IS THE FRONT OF THE BOAT.

GOD__ __ O__ __ __ __ __ TO SAVE NOAH.

NOAH OPENED A __ __ __ __ __ O TO SEND OUT A DOVE.

THE TOWER OF BABEL

PEOPLE BUILT A HIGH TOWER TO PROVE HOW POWERFUL AND SMART THEY WERE — BUT GOD WAS NOT PLEASED.

UNSCRAMBLE THE WORDS AND PUT THEM IN PROPER ORDER TO FIND OUT WHAT GOD DID TO STOP THEM.

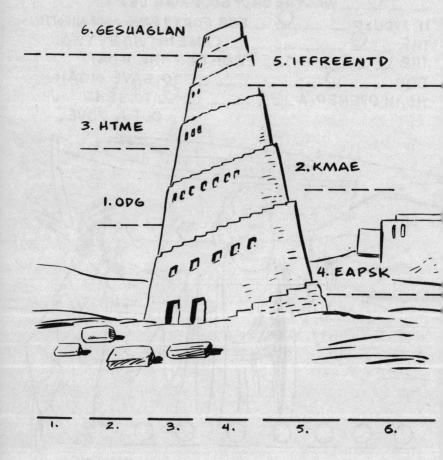

6. GESUAGLAN

5. IFFREENTD

3. HTME

2. KMAE

1. ODG

4. EAPSK

1. ___ 2. ___ 3. ___ 4. ___ 5. ___ 6. ___

ANSWER: GOD MADE THEM SPEAK DIFFERENT LANGUAGES.

WHATEVER HAPPENED TO JOSEPH?

USING THE CODE BELOW, FIND THE ANSWER.

A	B	C	D	E	F	G	H	I	J	K	L	M
26	25	24	23	22	21	20	19	18	17	16	15	14

N	O	P	Q	R	S	T	U	V	W	X	Y	Z
13	12	11	10	9	8	7	6	5	4	3	2	1

17 12 8 22 11 19 4 26 8 25 15 22 8 8 22 23

25 2 20 12 23 26 13 23 14 26 23 22 26

9 6 15 22 9 18 13 22 20 2 11 7 .

ANSWER: JOSEPH IS BLESSED BY GOD AND MADE A RULER IN EGYPT.

UNSCRAMBLE THE LETTERS BELOW TO FIND THE NAME OF:

THE SEVENTH BOOK OF THE BIBLE:

SJEUGD

___ ___ ___ ___ ___ ___

THE EIGHTH BOOK OF THE BIBLE:

HRTU

___ ___ ___ ___

THE NINTH BOOK OF THE BIBLE:

LSEA 1 UM

___ ___ ___ ___ ___ ___

THE TENTH BOOK OF THE BIBLE:

LM 2 USAE

___ ___ ___ ___ ___ ___

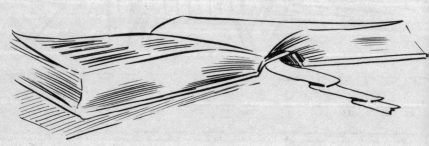

LOOK IN YOUR BIBLE

GOD REVEALED HIS NAME TO MOSES.
WHAT WAS GOD'S NAME ?

LOOK UP EXODUS 3: 13-14.

ANSWER:_____

ANSWER: "I AM WHO I AM."

USE THE CODE BELOW TO ANSWER THE QUESTIONS.

A B C D E F G H I J K L M
26 25 24 23 22 21 20 19 18 17 16 15 14

N O P Q R S T U V W X Y Z
13 12 11 10 9 8 7 6 5 4 3 2 1

THE NEXT BOOK IN THE
BIBLE AFTER EXODUS IS:

‾15‾ ‾22‾ ‾5‾ ‾18‾ ‾7‾ ‾18‾ ‾24‾ ‾6‾ ‾8‾

THIS MEANS:

‾26‾ ‾25‾ ‾12‾ ‾6‾ ‾7‾   ‾7‾ ‾19‾ ‾22‾
‾15‾ ‾22‾ ‾5‾ ‾18‾ ‾7‾ ‾22‾ ‾8‾

THE LEVITES ARE:

‾20‾ ‾12‾ ‾23‾ ‾8‾

‾11‾ ‾9‾ ‾18‾ ‾22‾ ‾8‾ ‾7‾ ‾8‾

LEVITICUS HELPS THE PEOPLE LIVE:

‾19‾ ‾12‾ ‾15‾ ‾2‾   ‾15‾ ‾18‾ ‾5‾ ‾22‾ ‾8‾

UNSCRAMBLE THE LETTERS BELOW TO NAME
THIS BOOK OF THE BIBLE

(IT'S A HARD ONE, SO YOU GET A LITTLE HELP ON THIS.)

Y D M E O U N T O E R

_ E _ _ _ E _ O _ _ O _ _

HOW MANY YEARS WERE THE ISRAELITES
IN THE DESERT?

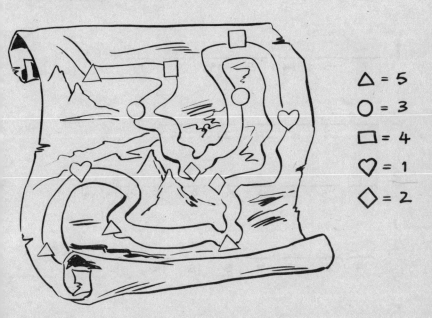

△ = 5

O = 3

□ = 4

♡ = 1

◇ = 2

△ + □ + O + ◇ + O + □ + ♡ + ◇ + △ + △ + ♡ + △ = ___

ANSWER: ___ YEARS

USE THE CODE BELOW TO NAME THE FIRST FIVE BOOKS
OF THE BIBLE.

A	B	C	D	E	F	G	H	I	J	K	L	M
1	2	3	4	5	6	7	8	9	10	11	12	13

N	O	P	Q	R	S	T	U	V	W	X	Y	Z
14	15	16	17	18	19	20	21	22	23	24	25	26

1. ___ ___ ___ ___ ___ ___ ___
   7   5   14   5   19   9   19

2. ___ ___ ___ ___ ___ ___
   5   24   15   4   21   19

3. ___ ___ ___ ___ ___ ___ ___ ___ ___
   12   5   22   9   20   9   3   21   19

4. ___ ___ ___ ___ ___ ___ ___
   14   21   13   2   5   18   19

5. ___ ___ ___ ___ ___ ___ ___ ___ ___ ___ ___
   4   5   21   20   5   18   15   14   15   13   25

USE THE CODE BELOW TO ANSWER THE QUESTIONS.

A	B	C	D	E	F	G	H	I	J	K	L	M
26	25	24	23	22	21	20	19	18	17	16	15	14

N	O	P	Q	R	S	T	U	V	W	X	Y	Z
13	12	11	10	9	8	7	6	5	4	3	2	1

WHO SHOWED HIMSELF TO MOSES IN THE BURNING BUSH?

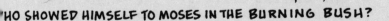

__ __ __ __ __ __ __ __ __ __ __ __ __ __ __ __ __
7 19 22 26 13 20 22 15 12 21 7 19 22 15 12 9 23

WHO IS THE ANGEL OF THE LORD?

__ __ __ __ __
7 22 8 6 8

WHO IS JESUS?

__ __ __
20 12 23

UNSCRAMBLE THE LETTERS
OF THESE BOOKS OF THE BIBLE

CTUSLEIVI Ⓞ __ __ __ __ Ⓞ __ __ __ __

YONEUTERDMO
__ __ __ Ⓞ __ __ __ __ __ __ __

DJGUES __ __ Ⓞ __ __ __

1KGINS __ __ __ __ Ⓞ

NSIGK 2 __ __ __ __ __

NSICOECHRL __ __ __ __ __ __ __ __ Ⓞ

AERZ __ __ __ Ⓞ

HNAEIHME Ⓞ __ __ __ __ __ __ __ . __

REESHT __ __ Ⓞ __ __ __ __

OJB __ __ __

SPMSLA __ __ Ⓞ __ Ⓞ __

SPBRREVO __ __ __ __ Ⓞ __ __ __

PUT THE CIRCLED LETTERS IN THE RIGHT ORDER.
YOU'LL FIND THESE BOOKS OF THE BIBLE IN THE:

Ⓞ Ⓞ Ⓞ   Ⓞ Ⓞ Ⓞ Ⓞ Ⓞ Ⓞ   Ⓞ Ⓞ Ⓞ

USE THE CODE BELOW TO ANSWER THE QUESTIONS.

A	B	C	D	E	F	G	H	I	J	K	L	M
26	25	24	23	22	21	20	19	18	17	16	15	14

N	O	P	Q	R	S	T	U	V	W	X	Y	Z
13	12	11	10	9	8	7	6	5	4	3	2	1

NAME THE BOOK THAT COMES
AFTER PSALMS.

__ __ __ __ __ __ __ __
11 9 12 5 22 9 25 8

WHO WROTE MOST OF THE
BOOK OF PROVERBS?

__ __ __ __
16 18 13 20

__ __ __ __ __ __ __
8 12 15 12 14 12 13

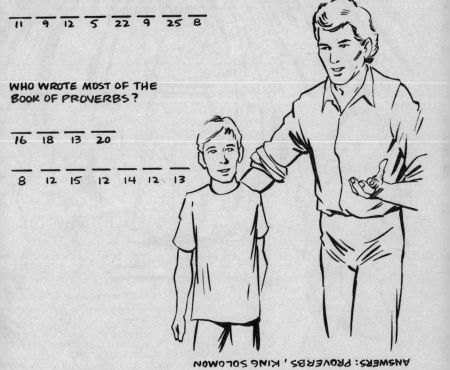

ANSWERS: PROVERBS, KING SOLOMON

LOOK IN YOUR BIBLE
LOOKS LIKE DANIEL IS IN A LOT OF DANGER!
FIND OUT WHAT HAPPENS -- THEN COLOR THE PICTURE.

READ DANIEL 6:1-24.

THESE THREE WERE PUT INTO A FIERY FURNACE BY KING NEBUCHADNEZZAR— BUT THEY WEREN'T EVEN SINGED!

WHO WERE THEY? USE THE CODE BELOW TO FIND OUT.

A	B	C	D	E	F
1	2	3	4	5	6

G	H	I	J	K	L
7	8	9	10	11	12

M	N	O	P	Q	R
13	14	15	16	17	18

S	T	U	V
19	20	21	22

W	X	Y	Z
23	24	25	26

— — — — — — — — '
19 8 1 4 18 1 3 8

— — — — — — — **AND** — — — — — — — —
3 5 19 8 1 3 8   1 2 5 4 14 5 7 15

(GOOD LUCK PRONOUNCING THESE!!)

ANSWERS: SHADRACH, MESHACH, ABEDNEGO

WHAT IS A PSALM?

CROSS OUT EVERY LETTER THAT APPEARS FOUR TIMES IN THE PUZZLE. COPY THE REST OF THE LETTERS, IN ORDER, TO FIND THE ANSWER.

A D S P F C
F C P D O A
C N A C F D
P D F A G P

A PSALM IS A _____ .

READ PSALM 23, THEN DRAW YOURSELF INTO THE PICTURE

SOLVE THE PUZZLE

_ESSE   DAVID'S FATHER
1

PHILISTIN_S   ISRAEL'S ENEMY
2

_AUL   KING OF ISRAEL
3

M_SIC   DAVID USES THIS TO COMFORT SAUL
4

_AMUEL   GOD'S PROPHET
5

_SRAEL   GOD'S NATION
6

_ONS OF JESSE   DAVID'S BROTHERS
7

_ORD   GOD
8

G_LIATH   GIANT PHILISTIN
9

WA_   ISRAEL FIGHTS
10

_AVID   GOD'S NEW KIN
11

WHAT DOES IT SAY?

_ _ _ _ _   _ _   _ _ _ _
1 2 3 4 5   6 7   8 9 10 11

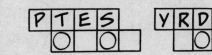

WORD JUMBLE

O	P	H	
	◯	◯	

P	T	E	S
	◯		◯

Y	R	D	
		◯	

HOW DAVID FLED FROM JERUSALEM

ON HIS ◯ ◯ ◯ ◯ ◯

USE THE CODE BELOW TO FIND THE NAMES OF JESUS'
EARTHLY PARENTS.

A	B	C	D	E	F	G
26	25	24	23	22	21	20

H	I	J	K	L	M	N
19	18	17	16	15	14	13

O	P	Q	R	S	T	U
12	11	10	9	8	7	6

V	W	X	Y	Z
5	4	3	2	1

$\overline{14}$ $\overline{26}$ $\overline{9}$ $\overline{2}$

AND

$\overline{17}$ $\overline{12}$ $\overline{8}$ $\overline{22}$ $\overline{11}$ $\overline{19}$

JESUS AT THE TEMPLE

HOW OLD WAS JESUS THE FIRST TIME HE WENT TO THE TEMPLE? LOOK AT THE NUMBERED BRICKS, AND SOLVE THE QUESTION BELOW.

☐ + ☐ + ☐ + △ + ◇ + ☐ + ◇ + ☐ = _____

CHECK LUKE 2: 41-52 TO MAKE SURE YOU HAVE THE RIGHT ANSWER

USE THE CODE BELOW TO FIND OUT WHAT JESUS
SAID TO DRIVE AWAY SATAN'S TEMPTATIONS.

IT IS
WRITTEN!

A B C D E F G
1 2 3 4 5 6 7
H I J K L M N
8 9 10 11 12 13 14
O P Q R S T U
15 16 17 18 19 20 21
V W X Y Z
22 23 24 25 26

1. $\overline{13}$ $\overline{1}$ $\overline{14}$ $\overline{4}$ $\overline{15}$ $\overline{5}$ $\overline{19}$ $\overline{14}$ $\overline{15}$ $\overline{20}$ $\overline{12}$ $\overline{9}$ $\overline{22}$ $\overline{5}$ $\overline{15}$ $\overline{14}$

$\overline{2}$ $\overline{18}$ $\overline{5}$ $\overline{1}$ $\overline{4}$ $\overline{1}$ $\overline{12}$ $\overline{15}$ $\overline{14}$ $\overline{5}$.

2. $\overline{4}$ $\overline{15}$ $\overline{14}$ $\overline{15}$ $\overline{20}$ $\overline{16}$ $\overline{21}$ $\overline{20}$ $\overline{20}$ $\overline{8}$ $\overline{5}$ $\overline{12}$ $\overline{15}$ $\overline{18}$ $\overline{4}$ $\overline{25}$ $\overline{15}$ $\overline{21}$ $\overline{18}$

$\overline{7}$ $\overline{15}$ $\overline{4}$ $\overline{20}$ $\overline{15}$ $\overline{20}$ $\overline{8}$ $\overline{5}$ $\overline{20}$ $\overline{5}$ $\overline{19}$ $\overline{20}$.

3. $\overline{23}$ $\overline{15}$ $\overline{18}$ $\overline{19}$ $\overline{8}$ $\overline{9}$ $\overline{16}$ $\overline{20}$ $\overline{8}$ $\overline{5}$ $\overline{12}$ $\overline{15}$ $\overline{18}$ $\overline{4}$ $\overline{25}$ $\overline{15}$ $\overline{21}$ $\overline{18}$

$\overline{7}$ $\overline{15}$ $\overline{4}$, $\overline{1}$ $\overline{14}$ $\overline{4}$ $\overline{19}$ $\overline{5}$ $\overline{18}$ $\overline{22}$ $\overline{5}$ $\overline{8}$ $\overline{9}$ $\overline{13}$ $\overline{15}$ $\overline{14}$ $\overline{12}$ $\overline{25}$.

JESUS HAS A MESSAGE FOR YOU.

UNSCRAMBLE THE WORDS, THEN PUT THE LETTERS IN THE MATCHING SHAPES BELOW.

SJESU — ♡ — — — —

HTTRU — — ☆ — — —

YWA — — ⬡ —

ELIF — ☐ — — —

NSI — — —

YHOL — △ ◯ —

EVLO — — ◇ —

DLRO — △ — —

☐ ◯ △ ◇ ♡   ⬡ △ ☆ __ __ __ .

WHAT'S JESUS DOING?

ADD OR SUBTRACT THE PICTURE CLUES AND LETTERS
ACCORDING TO THE + OR — SIGNS TO FIND THE ANSWER.

— AT + E = _____

— P, G + S = _____

T + — C, H + ING = _____

— E = _____

— UM + 1 — NE + D = _____

UNSCRAMBLE THE LETTERS TO FIND OUT THE NAMES OF SOME OF JESUS' DISCIPLES.
(HINT: LOOK UP MATTHEW 10:2–4.)

LIPPHI ________

STHOAM ________

MAJSE ________

THRABOOLMEW ______________

NSMIO ________

SUJDA ________

TRPEE ________

NJHO ________

ANSWERS: PHILIP, THOMAS, JAMES, BARTHOLOMEW, SIMON, JUDAS, PETER, JOHN

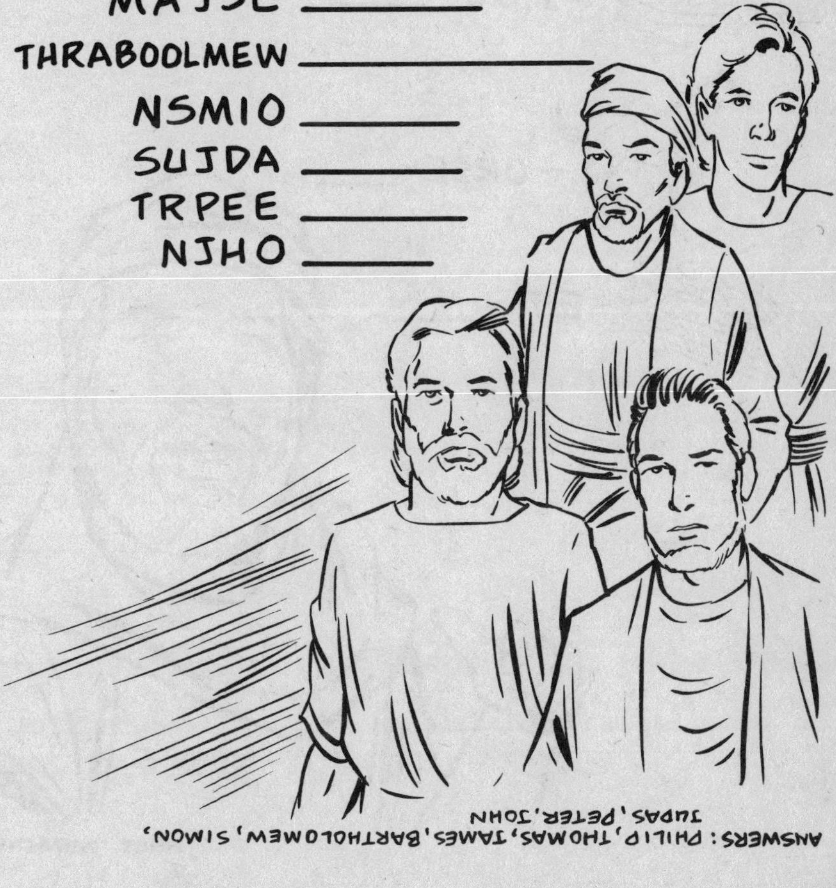

WHO THOUGHT HE WAS JESUS' FAVORITE
DISCIPLE?

ADD AND SUBTRACT THE PICTURE CLUES AND LETTERS.

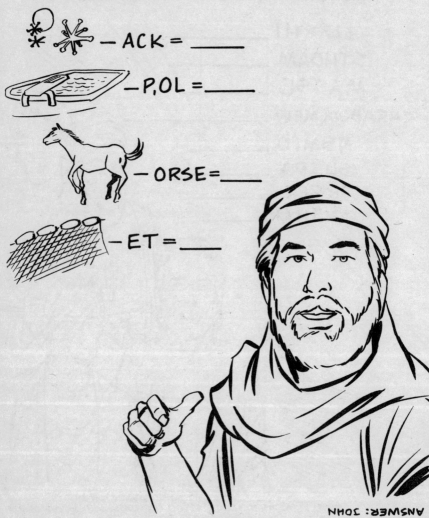

— ACK = _____

— P,OL = _____

— ORSE = _____

— ET = _____

USE THE CODE BELOW TO FIND THE NAMES OF THE THREE
PERSONS OF THE TRINITY.

A	B	C	D	E	F
1	2	3	4	5	6
G	H	I	J	K	L
7	8	9	10	11	12
M	N	O	P	Q	R
13	14	15	16	17	18
S	T	U	V	W	X
19	20	21	22	23	24
Y	Z
25	26

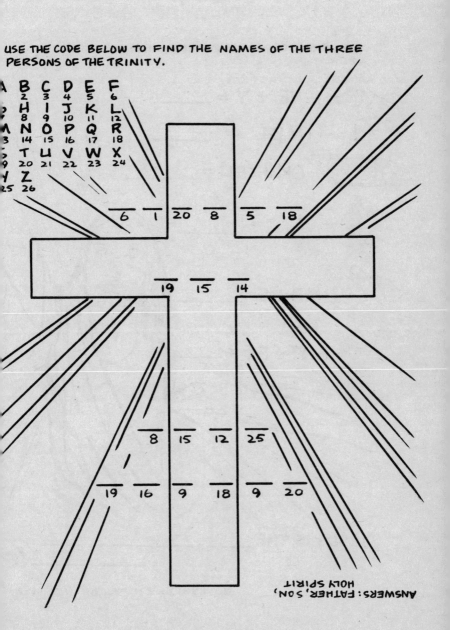

$\overline{6}$ $\overline{1}$ $\overline{20}$ $\overline{8}$ $\overline{5}$ $\overline{18}$

$\overline{19}$ $\overline{15}$ $\overline{14}$

$\overline{8}$ $\overline{15}$ $\overline{12}$ $\overline{25}$

$\overline{19}$ $\overline{16}$ $\overline{9}$ $\overline{18}$ $\overline{9}$ $\overline{20}$

ADD OR SUBTRACT THE PICTURE CLUES AND LETTERS.

— VE + Y = _____

— 1MBL = _____

— CK + TH = _____

— H = _____

— UMB + E = _____

— GHT + FE = _____

JESUS IS THE _____ , ___ _____ , _____ ___ ___ !

USING THE CODE BELOW, FIND THE ANSWERS AND FINISH THE SENTENCES.

A	B	C	D	E	F	G	H	I	J	K	L	M
26	25	24	23	22	21	20	19	18	17	16	15	14

N	O	P	Q	R	S	T	U	V	W	X	Y	Z
13	12	11	10	9	8	7	6	5	4	3	2	1

THE BOOK OF ACTS TELLS WHAT HAPPENED TO $\frac{}{17}\frac{}{22}\frac{}{8}\frac{}{6}\frac{}{8}$'

$\frac{}{21}\frac{}{12}\frac{}{15}\frac{}{15}\frac{}{12}\frac{}{4}\frac{}{22}\frac{}{9}\frac{}{8}$ AFTER HIS RESURRECTION.

PETER WAS USED BY GOD TO $\frac{}{25}\frac{}{6}\frac{}{18}\frac{}{15}\frac{}{23}\frac{}{7}\frac{}{19}\frac{}{22}$

$\frac{}{24}\frac{}{19}\frac{}{6}\frac{}{9}\frac{}{24}\frac{}{19}$.

THE $\frac{}{20}\frac{}{12}\frac{}{8}\frac{}{11}\frac{}{22}\frac{}{15}$ $\frac{}{12}\frac{}{21}$ $\frac{}{24}\frac{}{19}\frac{}{9}\frac{}{18}\frac{}{8}\frac{}{7}$

SPREAD ALL OVER THE WORLD.

UNSCRAMBLE THE WORDS

LAPU   _Paul_

NVOIIS   _vision_

KSEE   _seek_

RLEETT   _letter_

HJSEIW   _Jewish_

LJIA   _Jail_

ANSWERS: PAUL, VISION, SEEK, LETTER, JEWISH, JAIL

ADD OR SUBTRACT THE PICTURE
CLUES AND LETTERS.

IN THE BOOK OF ACTS, SAUL'S NAME WAS CHANGED TO

− IG = __P__

− PPLE = __A__

− SA, CER = __U__

− BIB, E = __L__

HOLY BIBLE

DID YOU KNOW?
ADD OR SUBTRACT THE PICTURE CLUES AND LETTERS.

– T + SUS = _____

– M,CE + S = _____

– BA + E = _____

– UN + – C,R,W = _____

– F = _____

G + – R = _____

MATCH THE COLUMNS.

ANGEL

SPEAR

BRIDLE

TOUNGES OF
FIRE

CHAINS

SLING

ARK

MATCH THE COLUMNS

HARP

CROWN

THRONE

ARMOR

SLING

SWORD

MATCH THE COLUMNS

THORNS

PALM BRANCH

PIG

COLT

THE WORD

MATCH THE COLUMNS

PYRAMID

PALM TRE[E]

HELMET

SWORD

CLOAK

MATCH THE COLUMNS

STAFF

WATER JUG

FISHING BOAT

NET

SANDAL

ANGEL

PAUL'S MISSIONARY JOURNEY
HELP PAUL GET TO HIS DESTINATION OF ROME.

JESUS WAS ARRESTED IN THE GARDEN OF
GETHSEMANE. PETER TRIED TO GET AWAY FROM
THE SOLDIERS. HELP HIM FIND HIS WAY OUT.

EXIT

ADD THE NUMBERS TO FIND OUT HOW
MANY DAYS JESUS WAS IN THE DESERT.

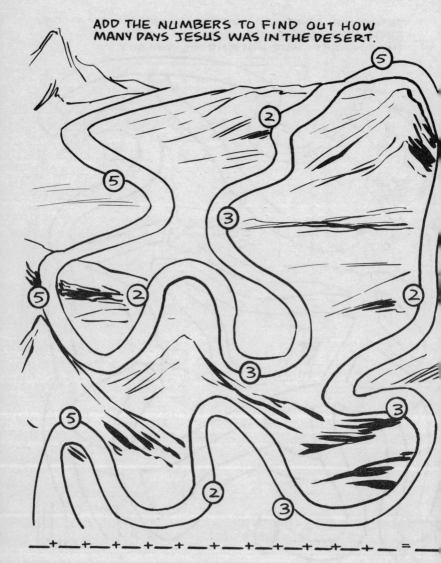

_ + _ + _ + _ + _ + _ + _ + _ + _ + _ + _ = _

ANSWER: FORTY

AS YOU GO THROUGH THE MAZE, PICK UP EACH LETTER AND FIND THE
<u>ONLY</u> WAY WE GET TO HEAVEN.

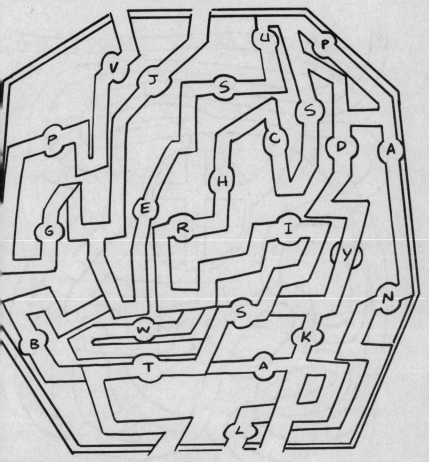

BY BELIEVING AND TRUSTING
IN: _____ ALONE!

MANY PATHS THAT LEAD NOWHERE – ONLY ONE SURE WAY.
CAN YOU FIND IT?

DANIEL AND THE ISRAELITES WERE TAKEN AS PRISONERS
OF WAR TO BABYLON - A BIG AND BUSY CITY.
HELP DANIEL FIND HIS NEW APARTMENT.

HELP THE ISRAELITES GET TO THE PROMISED LAND.

JOSEPH WAS SOLD AS A SLAVE BY HIS BROTHERS AND
TAKEN TO EGYPT. HELP THE CARAVAN GET THROUGH
THE DUNES AND AROUND THE DANGERS.

HELP DAVID ESCAPE SAUL

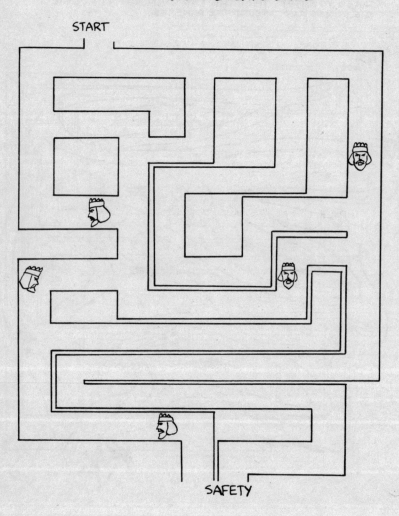

START

SAFETY

HELP DAVID GET OUT OF JERUSALEM

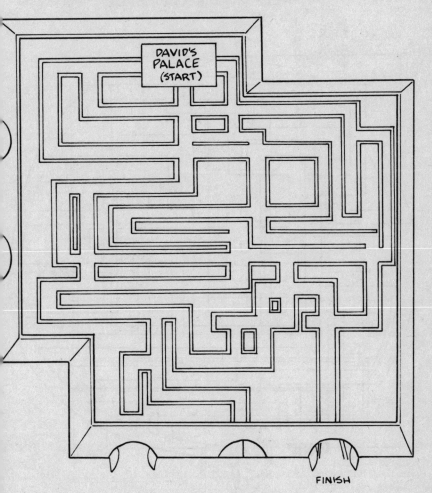

HELP SAMUEL FIND THE SON OF JESSE THAT GOD HAS CHOSEN

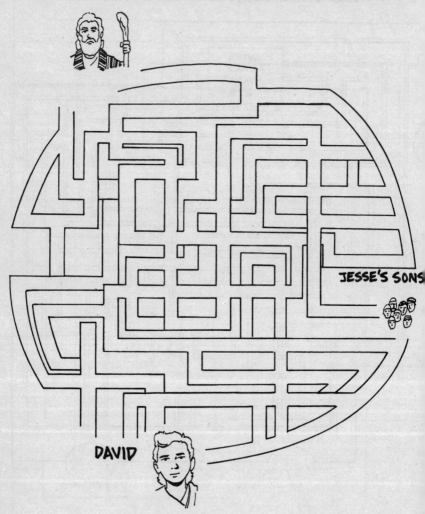

JESSE'S SONS

DAVID

ON TO JERUSALEM !

START

FINISH

HELP JOSEPH, MARY AND JESUS FIND THE WAY TO EGYPT

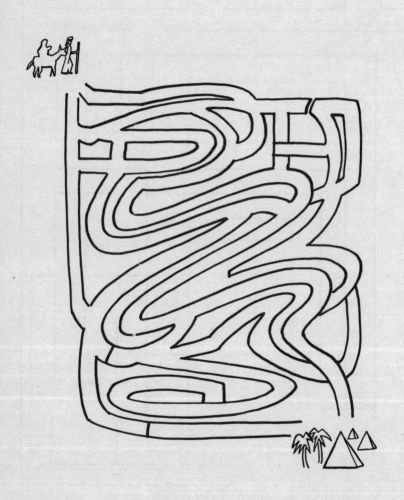

HOW TO DRAW DAVID

START WITH SIMPLE SHAPES

DRAW GUIDELINES _LIGHTLY_

DRAW DETAILS

FINISH AND ERASE GUIDELINES

NOW - TRY ON YOUR OWN PIECE OF PAPER!

HOW TO DRAW JESUS

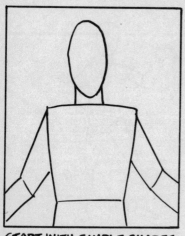

START WITH SIMPLE SHAPES

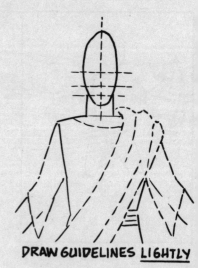

DRAW GUIDELINES <u>LIGHTLY</u>

ADD DETAILS: EYES, NOSE
MOUTH, EARS, BEARD,
HAIR AND CLOTHING

FINISH AND ERASE GUIDELINES

NOAH BUILT THE ARK

PUT THE PICTURES IN ORDER AS THEY HAPPENED FIRST, SECOND, THIRD AND LAST. WRITE THE CORRECT NUMBER IN THE BLANK SPACE UNDER EACH PICTURE.

#_____

#_____

#_____

#_____

ANSWER: 3, 2, 1, 4

ABRAM IS MOVING
GOD HAS TOLD ABRAM TO MOVE BY FAITH. WHAT WILL HE TAKE WITH HIM?

COLOR ABRAM AND THE CORRECT ITEMS.

JOSEPH WAS GIVEN A COAT OF MANY COLORS.
USE THE COLOR GUIDE BELOW TO COLOR IT YOURSELF.

1 = RED   2 = YELLOW   3 = BLUE   4 = GREEN   5 = ORANGE   6 = PURPLE

FIND THE DIFFERENCES

MOSES COMES DOWN THE MOUNTAIN WITH THE TEN COMMANDMENTS
OF GOD. CIRCLE THE DIFFERENCES.

SNAKES IN THE DESERT

CIRCLE THE SEVEN DEADLY SNAKES.

FIND THE DIFFERENCES

FIND THE DIFFERENCES

SOLOMON'S TEMPLE

FIND AT LEAST SIX DIFFERENCES IN THE TWO PICTURES BELOW.

JESUS IN THE MANGER

WHAT'S WRONG WITH THIS PICTURE?

ZACCHEUS, A WEALTHY TAX COLLECTOR, CLIMBED A TREE
TO GET A BETTER LOOK AT JESUS. BUT, THIS IS A VERY
STRANGE TREE. FIND AND CIRCLE WHAT DOESN'T BELONG.

FIND ALL THE BREAD AND FISH

FIND THE DIFFERENCES

WHAT'S WRONG WITH THIS PICTURE?

JESUS HAD FIVE THOUSAND PEOPLE TO FEED. ONLY TWO OF THE ITEMS BELOW ARE WHAT HE USED TO MULTIPLY WITH A MIRACLE. CIRCLE WHAT BELONGS.

ANSWER: HE USED THE BREAD AND FISHES.

PETER'S GONE FISHING AND HIS NET IS FULL - BUT SOME
OF HIS CATCH, HE COULD NOT SELL AT THE FISH MARKET!
CIRCLE WHAT DOESN'T BELONG.

PETER'S IN JAIL
FOR TALKING ABOUT JESUS!

BUT GOD HAS SENT AN ANGEL TO SET HIM FREE.
WHICH ONE IS THE ANGEL OF GOD?
COLOR HIM AND PETER.

FIND THE DIFFERENCES
PAUL ON HIS JOURNEY

HELP PAUL FIND HIS SHADOW.

DRESS DAVID FOR BATTLE

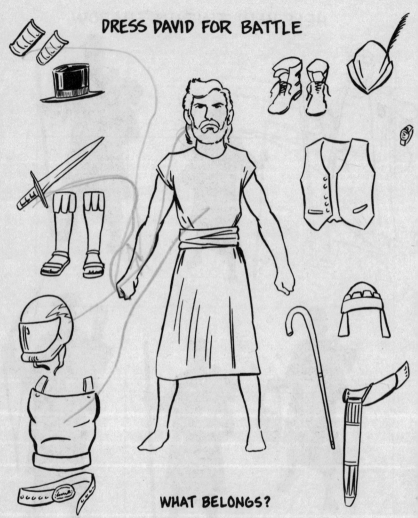

WHAT BELONGS?

CUT OUT AND GLUE OR DRAW IT ON

DRAW MOSES

USING THE LEFT SIDE AS A GUIDE, DRAW, THEN COLOR, MOSES.

FINISH THE PICTURE
THEN
LOOK IN YOUR BIBLE.

THIS MAN WITH THE JAWBONE — DO YOU KNOW WHO HE IS?
HIS NAME IS _____ .
LOOK IN JUDGES 15: 15-16 FOR THE ANSWER.

ANSWER: SAMSON

DRAW FOR YOURSELF

FINISH THE OTHER SIDE.

DRAW FOR YOURSELF

USING WHAT IS IN EACH SQUARE, GO TO THE FOLLOWING
PAGE AND COPY THIS PICTURE.

COPY FROM THE PREVIOUS PAGE.

DRAW FOR YOURSELF

USING THE SQUARES AS A GUIDE, GO TO THE FOLLOWING PAGE AND COPY THIS PICTURE.

DRAW FOR YOURSELF

USING WHAT IS IN EACH SQUARE, GO TO THE FOLLOWING PAGE AND COPY THE PICTURE.

"I STAND AT THE DOOR AND KNOCK. IF ANYONE HEARS MY VOICE AND OPENS THE DOOR, I WILL COME IN AND EAT WITH HIM AND HE WITH ME." REVELATIONS 3:20

DRAW FROM THE PREVIOUS PAGE.

DRAW FOR YOURSELF

USING WHAT IS IN EACH SQUARE, GO TO THE FOLLOWING
PAGE AND COPY THE PICTURE.

DRAW FROM THE PREVIOUS PAGE.

COLOR BY NUMBER

JESUS ALWAYS TOOK TIME TO PRAY

1 = FLESH TONE   2 = BLUE   3 = BROWN   4 = LIGHT BLUE
5 = LIGHT BROWN 6 = GREEN 7 = YELLOW 8 = DARK GREEN
9 = GREY

FINISH THE PICTURE
JESUS DIED ON A CROSS FOR OUR SINS.

FINISH THE PICTURE

THEN COLOR.

Answer Pages

1

TRAVEL THE PATH THAT MAKES A SENTENCE.

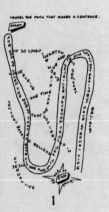

2

AFTER GOING THROUGH THE MAZE ON THE PREVIOUS PAGE, FILL IN THE BLANKS BELOW TO FINISH THE SENTENCE.

"FOR GOD SO LOVED THE WORLD THAT HE GAVE HIS ONE AND ONLY SON, THAT WHOEVER BELIEVES IN HIM SHALL NOT PERISH BUT HAVE ETERNAL LIFE."

JOHN 3:16

3

FIND THE WORDS BELOW IN THE WORDSEARCH PUZZLE.

```
J R U A M D C I W A U I H X
M G O T P N S C S M L E I X
S O E B F T L O V E D Y W G
E D R K T B J F C V T G H K
Q L Q O S E H G P B N I P L
E A D B E L I E V E S D M T
C H R X N B C O G K O L O
L N O R L D A S U D H P B W
W R Q G U H O A M V K L A I
I N B S O T Y N P W A I C Z
P K L Y V L O D J X Z F O S
Z P E R I S H B N V T E K V
N F I S G F V X N C W B H F
P E T E R N A L T O B G Q J
D N R I G Z M E X V N V R Z
```

ETERNAL   HIM
WORLD   LIFE
SON   BELIEVES
PERISH   HIS
GOD   LOVED

4

"FOR GOD SO LOVED THE WORLD..."

FINISH THE PICTURE.

5

FIND THE WORDS TO THIS VERSE IN THE WORDSEARCH BELOW.

"FOR ALL HAVE SINNED AND FALL SHORT OF THE GLORY OF GOD."

ROMANS 3:23

6

FIND THE WORDS TO THIS VERSE IN THE WORDSEARCH BELOW.

"...WHILE WE WERE STILL SINNERS, CHRIST DIED FOR US."

ROMANS 5:8.

7

USE THE CODE CHART TO MATCH THE NUMBERS WITH LETTERS. USE THE COLUMN GOING DOWN, FIRST, THEN WRITE THE LETTERS IN THE BLANKS.

	1	2	3	4	5	6
1	A	F	K	P	U	Z
2	B	G	L	Q	V	
3	C	H	M	R	W	
4	D	I	N	S	X	
5	E	J	O	T	Y	

"FOR THE WAGES OF SIN IS DEATH, BUT THE GIFT OF GOD IS ETERNAL LIFE IN CHRIST JESUS OUR LORD"

Romans 6:23

8

CONNECT-THE-DOTS

9

TRAVEL THE PATH THAT MAKES A SENTENCE.

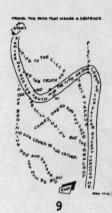

START

END

10

AFTER GOING THROUGH THE MAZE ON THE PREVIOUS PAGE, FILL IN THE BLANKS BELOW TO FINISH THE SENTENCE.

"I AM THE WAY AND THE TRUTH AND THE LIFE. NO ONE COMES TO THE FATHER EXCEPT THROUGH ME."

John 14:6

NOW FIND THE UNDERLINED WORDS IN THE WORDSEARCH BELOW.

11

USE THE CODE CHART TO MATCH THE NUMBERS WITH LETTERS. USE THE COLUMN GOING DOWN, FIRST, THEN WRITE THE LETTERS IN THE BLANKS.

	1	2	3	4	5	6
1	A	F	K	P	U	Z
2	B	G	L	Q	V	
3	C	H	M	R	W	
4	D	I	N	S	X	
5	E	J	O	T	Y	

John 5:24a

"I TELL YOU THE TRUTH, WHOEVER HEARS MY WORD AND BELIEVES HIM WHO SENT ME HAS ETERNAL LIFE AND WILL NOT BE CONDEMNED..."

12

FINISH THE PICTURE OF JESUS.

13

TRAVEL THE PATH THAT MAKES A SENTENCE.

START

END

Romans 10:9

14

AFTER GOING THROUGH THE MAZE ON THE PREVIOUS PAGE, FILL IN THE BLANKS BELOW TO FINISH THE SENTENCE.

"IF YOU CONFESS WITH YOUR MOUTH 'JESUS IS LORD' AND BELIEVE IN YOUR HEART THAT GOD RAISED HIM FROM THE DEAD, YOU WILL BE SAVED."

Romans 10:9

15

FIND THE WORDS BELOW IN THE WORDSEARCH PUZZLE.

LORD
HEART
DEAD
CONFESS
SAVED

RAISED
MOUTH
BELIEVE
JESUS

16

COLOR THE PICTURE.

16

17

JESUS IS KNOCKING AT THE DOOR OF YOUR HEART. WHAT SHOULD YOU DO?

USE THE CODE CHART BELOW TO MATCH THE CODES WITH LETTERS. USE THE COLUMN ACROSS DOWN FIRST. THEN WRITE THE LETTERS IN THE BLANKS TO COMPLETE THE VERSE.
THEN YOU WILL KNOW WHAT TO DO!

	1	2	3	4	5	6
1	A	H	I	P	Q	X	Y
2	B	G	J	O	R	W	Z
3	C	F	K	N	S	V	
4	D	E	L	M	T	U	

"HERE I AM! I STAND AT THE DOOR AND KNOCK."

CONTINUED NEXT PAGE...

17

18

CONTINUED FROM PREVIOUS PAGE.

	1	2	3	4	5	6
1	A	H	I	P	Q	X	Y
2	B	G	J	O	R	W	Z
3	C	F	K	N	S	V	
4	D	E	L	M	T	U	

"IF ANYONE HEARS MY VOICE AND OPENS THE DOOR, I WILL COME IN AND EAT WITH HIM, AND HE WITH ME."

REVELATION 3:20

18

19

19

20

DO YOU KNOW JESUS LOVES YOU? DO YOU KNOW HOW MUCH JESUS LOVES YOU? HE LOVES YOU SO MUCH THAT HE DIED TO PAY THE PRICE FOR YOUR SIN. THERE IS ONLY ONE SIN THAT GOD WILL NOT FORGIVE. THAT SIN IS NOT BELIEVING IN JESUS AND WHAT HE DID FOR YOU AND ALL OF US. WITHOUT JESUS, WITHOUT ACCEPTING THAT HE DIED FOR US, NO ONE CAN GO TO HEAVEN.

THREE DAYS AFTER JESUS DIED, HE WAS RAISED TO NEW LIFE. HE WANTS TO SHARE THAT WITH US TOO! HE WANTS TO GIVE US NEW LIFE ... ETERNAL LIFE!

DO YOU WANT TO ASK JESUS TO COME INTO YOUR HEART AND YOUR LIFE? ALL YOU NEED TO DO IS ASK HIM. YOU COULD SAY A PRAYER LIKE THIS:

DEAR JESUS,

I KNOW I AM A SINNER AND THAT YOU DIED FOR ALL MY SINS. I KNOW YOU ROSE FROM THE DEAD. JESUS, I ASK YOU HOW TO COME INTO MY HEART AND TAKE CONTROL OF MY LIFE.
THANK YOU FOR ALL YOU HAVE DONE FOR ME.
TEACH ME YOUR WAYS, JESUS, AND HELP ME TO GROW UP WITH YOU.

IN JESUS' NAME, I PRAY, AMEN.

IF YOU HAVE NEVER INVITED JESUS INTO YOUR HEART AND LIFE BUT YOU WANT TO NOW, GO TO THE NEXT PAGE AND WRITE OUT YOUR PRAYER IN YOUR OWN WORDS. JUST TELL JESUS HOW YOU REALLY FEEL.

20

21

MY VERY OWN PRAYER TO INVITE JESUS INTO MY HEART AND LIFE.

DATE: _____

DEAR LORD JESUS,

_____
_____
_____
_____
_____
_____
_____
_____
_____
_____

IN JESUS' NAME, AMEN.

_____
YOUR NAME

21

22

DID YOU INVITE JESUS INTO YOUR HEART?

FIND YOUR WAY TO JESUS!

22

23

WOW! IF YOU ASKED JESUS INTO YOUR LIFE, YOU ARE NOW A CHILD OF GOD!

LET'S LEARN HOW TO GET TO KNOW JESUS BETTER.

UNSCRAMBLE THE WORDS BELOW TO FIND OUT HOW TO BEGIN.

1) TO BECOME A CHILD OF GOD, YOU HAD TO ASK JESUS INTO YOUR HEART. THIS IS CALLED __PRAYING__.
   IYANARF

2) PRAYING IS __TALKING__ WITH GOD.
   GTINALK

3) JUST LIKE YOU TALK WITH YOUR MOM OR DAD, GOD __WANTS__ YOU TO __TALK__ WITH HIM.
   TWNAS   KTLA

4) IT DOES NOT STOP THERE. GOD WANTS TO TALK TO YOU! JESUS SPEAKS TO YOU THROUGH HIS __WORD__.
   DRWO

5) THE ONLY WAY TO REALLY KNOW JESUS IS TO __READ__ ABOUT __HIM__.
   ARDE   IMH

6) YOU READ ABOUT __JESUS__ IN THE HOLY __BIBLE__.
   EBILB   JSSUE

23

24

IN THE FOLLOWING WORDSEARCH PUZZLE, FIND AND CIRCLE THE WORDS LISTED.

THEY CAN BE FOUND IN LINES GOING FORWARD, BACKWARD, UP, DOWN, OR DIAGONALLY.

LOVED	HEARS	EAT
KNOCK	VOICE	ANYONE
DOOR	HIM	STAND

24

WHAT HAVE YOU LEARNED ABOUT
BEING A CHILD OF GOD?

FIND AND CIRCLE THE WORDS LISTED
BELOW.

PRAY   WORD   TALK

READ   JESUS   GOD

BIBLE   SAVIOUR INVITE

25

CONNECT THE DOTS
AND FINISH THE PHRASE.

JESUS, THE L I O N OF JUDAH!

26

ACROSS

1. GOD _GAVE_ US HIS ONE AND ONLY S...

2. NOW WE CAN HAVE ETERNAL _LIFE_.

3. JESUS KNOCKS AT THE DOORS OF
   OUR _HEARTS_.

4. IF WE HAVE _INVITED_ HIM IN, HE
   WILL NEVER LEAVE US.

DOWN

5. WE ARE NOW A CHILD OF _GOD_.

6. WE TALK TO HIM BY _PRAYING_.

7. HE TALKS TO US THROUGH _HIS_
   WORD.

8. HIS WORD IS THE _BIBLE_.

WORD LIST

PRAYING   HEARTS

LIFE   BIBLE

GAVE   HIS

INVITED   GOD

27

28

SOMETIMES, IT'S NOT EASY TO READ THE
BIBLE EVERY DAY. OTHER THINGS
WILL TRY TO GET IN THE WAY, BUT IF YOU
REALLY WANT TO GROW AS A CHRISTIAN, IT IS
BEST TO READ IN GOD'S WORD EACH DAY.

FIND YOUR WAY TO THE BIBLE

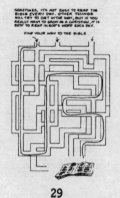

29

TRAVEL THE PATH THAT MAKES A SENTENCE

30

AFTER GOING THROUGH THE MAZE ON
THE PREVIOUS PAGE, FILL IN THE BLANKS
BELOW TO FINISH THE SENTENCE.

"WHEN THE _COUNSELOR_
COMES, _WHOM_ I WILL
SEND TO YOU FROM THE
FATHER, THE _SPIRIT_
OF _TRUTH_ WHO _GOES_
OUT FROM THE FATHER, HE
WILL _TESTIFY_
ABOUT ME."

JOHN 15:26

31

FIND THE WORDS BELOW IN THE
WORDSEARCH PUZZLE.

SPIRIT   WHOM   YOU

ABOUT   TRUTH   TESTIFY

GOES   COUNSELOR SEND

32

COLOR THE PICTURE

WHEN YOU BECOME A CHILD OF GOD,
WHERE DOES THE HOLY SPIRIT LIVE?

GO ON TO THE NEXT PAGE TO FIND
THE ANSWER.

33

USE THE CODE CHART BELOW TO MATCH
THE CODES WITH LETTERS. USE THE
COLUMN GOING DOWN, FIRST. THEN WRITE
THE LETTERS IN THE BLANKS.

	1	2	3	4	5	6	7
1	A	H	I	P	Q	X	Y
2	B	G	J	O	R	W	Z
3	C	F	K	N	S	V	
4	U	D	E	L	M	T	!

"DO YOU NOT KNOW
THAT YOUR BODY
IS A TEMPLE OF
THE HOLY SPIRIT,
WHO IS IN YOU
WHOM YOU HAVE
RECEIVED FROM GOD"
1 CORINTHIANS 6:19

34

THE HOLY SPIRIT ACTUALLY COMES TO
LIVE INSIDE YOU! YOUR BODY BECOMES
THE TEMPLE, OR DWELLING PLACE, OF GOD'S
SPIRIT.

THIS IS HARD TO UNDERSTAND BECAUSE
WE CAN'T SEE HIM, BUT IT IS TRUE. BECAUSE
THE BIBLE SAYS IT IS SO. MANY TIMES
THE HOLY SPIRIT MAKES HIS PRESENCE
KNOWN. WE CAN FEEL HIM AS HE GIVES
US HIS POWER AND STRENGTH TO LIVE
AS GOD WANTS US TO LIVE.

CONNECT-THE-DOTS

35

ONCE, OUR HUMAN SPIRITS WERE DEAD. WE
WERE BORN SPIRITUALLY DEAD. JESUS
GIVES US NEW LIFE IN OUR SPIRITS!

"FOR JUST AS THE FATHER RAISES THE
DEAD AND GIVES THEM LIFE, EVEN SO THE
SON GIVES LIFE TO WHOM HE IS PLEASED
TO GIVE IT."
John 5:21

GO TO THE NEXT PAGE. USING THE GRID
THE ABOVE PICTURE FOR YOURSELF.

36

FROM THE PREVIOUS PAGE, USE THE
GRID TO DRAW THE PICTURE FOR YOURSELF.

37

NOW THAT YOU ARE A CHRISTIAN, YOU MUST
LET THE HOLY SPIRIT TEACH YOU HOW TO
LIVE YOUR NEW LIFE. HOW DOES HE DO
THIS?

USE THE CODE CHART BELOW TO MATCH
THE CODES WITH LETTERS. USE THE
COLUMN GOING DOWN, FIRST. THEN WRITE
THE LETTERS IN THE BLANKS ON THE
FOLLOWING PAGE.

	1	2	3	4	5	6	7
1	A	B	C	D	E	F	G
2	H	I	J	K	L	M	N
3	O	P	Q	R	S	T	U
4	V	W	X	Y	Z		

WHAT YOU PUT INTO YOUR MIND, WHAT
YOU REAP OR WATCH OR LISTEN TO, IS
WHAT WILL COME OUT OF YOU. IF YOU
PUT GOD'S WORD IN, IF YOU READ THE
BIBLE REGULARLY, GOD'S CHARACTER
WILL COME OUT OF YOU IN THE WAYS YOU
THINK, ACT AND THE CHOICES YOU MAKE.

38

USING THE CODE CHART FROM THE
PREVIOUS PAGE, COMPLETE THE VERSE
BELOW.

"DO NOT CONFORM
ANY LONGER TO THE
PATTERN OF THIS
WORLD, BUT BE
TRANSFORMED BY
THE RENEWING
OF YOUR MIND."
ROMANS 12:2

39

COLOR THE PICTURE

BE CAREFUL IN YOUR CHOICES!

40

TRAVEL THE PATH THAT MAKES A SENTENCE.

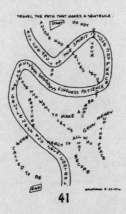

41

AFTER GOING THROUGH THE MAZE ON
THE PREVIOUS PAGE, FILL IN THE
BLANKS BELOW TO FINISH THE VERSE.

"BUT THE FRUIT OF
THE SPIRIT IS
LOVE, JOY,
PEACE,
PATIENCE,
KINDNESS,
GOODNESS,
FAITHFULNESS,
GENTLENESS,
AND SELF-CONTROL"

GALATIANS 5:22-23 a

42

43

FIND THE WORDS BELOW IN THE WORDSEARCH PUZZLE.

JOY
SELF-CONTROL
GENTLENESS
PEACE
FRUIT
FAITHFULNESS

KINDNESS
SPIRIT
PATIENCE
GOODNESS
LOVE

44

THE FRUIT OF THE SPIRIT

FILL IN THE BLANKS.

PATIENCE

GOODNESS

LOVE

FAITHFULNESS

SELF-CONTROL   PEACE

KINDNESS   JOY

GENTLENESS

45

YOU ALREADY KNOW THAT WHEN YOU BECOME A CHRISTIAN, THE HOLY SPIRIT COMES TO LIVE IN YOU. THE HOLY SPIRIT WILL LEAD YOU INTO GOD'S TRUTH, AND HE WILL DO THE WORK OF PRODUCING GOD'S CHARACTER IN YOU, IF YOU WILL LET HIM. YOU CAN DO THAT BY CHOOSING TO DO WHAT GOD WANTS RATHER THAN WHAT YOU WANT. THIS IS CALLED SURRENDERING, OR GIVING UP, TO GOD'S WILL.

GOD'S CHARACTER IS THE FRUIT OF THE SPIRIT.

UNSCRAMBLE THE WORDS BELOW TO FIND GOD'S CHARACTER, THE FRUIT OF THE SPIRIT.

OVLE — L O V E
OYJ — J O Y
PCEEA — P E A C E
TIEENCPA — P A T I E N C E
DNNESKSI — K I N D N E S S
OGDOSSNE — G O O D N E S S
HTAIFLUFNESS — F A I T H F U L N E S S
TNLEEEGSSN — G E N T L E N E S S
- RTNSFLEOCLO — S E L F - C O N T R O L

46

FIND YOUR WAY THROUGH THE OBSTACLES, THE THINGS OF THIS WORLD, THAT WILL TRY TO PULL YOU AWAY FROM WHAT GOD WOULD WANT YOU TO DO.

END

47

FINISH THE PICTURE

AS YOU START TO LIVE YOUR NEW LIFE AS GOD'S CHILD, IT IS IMPORTANT TO KNOW WHO YOUR ENEMIES ARE!

THE CHRISTIAN HAS THREE ENEMIES:
1. THE DEVIL
2. THE SINFUL NATURE (THE FLESH)
3. THE WORLD

A CHRISTIAN IN THIS WORLD IS LIKE A SOLDIER - A SOLDIER OF THE LORD. YOUR ONLY WEAPON IS THE BIBLE.

48

USE THE CODE CHART BELOW TO MATCH THE CODES WITH LETTERS. USE THE COLUMN GOING DOWN, FIRST, THEN WRITE THE LETTERS IN THE BLANKS.

	1	2	3	4	5	6	7
1	A	B	C	D	E	F	G
2	H	I	J	K	L	M	N
3	O	P	Q	R	S	T	U
4	V	W	X	Y	Z		

"BE SELF-CONTROLLED
AND ALERT YOUR
ENEMY THE DEVIL
PROWLS AROUND
LIKE A ROARING
LION LOOKING
FOR SOMEONE
TO DEVOUR."

49

OUR LORD NEVER LEAVES HIS CHILDREN HELPLESS. HE ALWAYS GIVES US A WAY TO STAND AGAINST OUR ENEMY THE DEVIL.
TO FIND OUT HOW, USE THE CODE CHART BELOW TO COMPLETE THE VERSE. USE THE COLUMN GOING DOWN FIRST.

	1	2	3	4	5	6	7
1	A	B	C	D	E	F	G
2	H	I	J	K	L	M	N
3	O	P	Q	R	S	T	U
4	V	W	X	Y	Z		

"SUBMIT YOUR-
SELVES THEN, TO
GOD. RESIST
THE DEVIL
AND HE WILL
FLEE FROM YOU."

JAMES 4:7

50

CONNECT-THE-DOTS

"... RESIST THE DEVIL, AND HE WILL FLEE..."

51

WHAT DO YOU NEED TO DO WHEN THE DEVIL TEMPTS YOU TO SIN?

AS YOU GO THROUGH THE MAZE, COLLECT THE LETTERS AND COMPLETE THE STATEMENT BELOW.

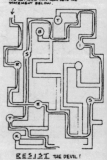

RESIST THE DEVIL!

52

WHAT IS THE DEVIL LIKE ?

AS YOU GO THROUGH THIS MAZE, COLLECT THE LETTERS AND COMPLETE THE STATEMENT BELOW.

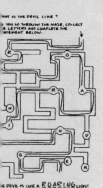

THE DEVIL IS LIKE A **ROARING** LION!

52

53

PSALM 119 : 104 - 105 GIVES ANOTHER DESCRIPTION OF GOD'S WORD, THE BIBLE. USE THE CODE BELOW TO COMPLETE THESE TWO VERSES. USE THE COLUMN GOING DOWN FIRST.

	1	2	3	4	5	6	7
1	A	B	C	D	E	F	G
2	H	I	J	K	L	M	N
3	O	P	Q	R	S	T	U
4	V	W	X	Y	Z		

"I GAIN UNDER-
STANDING FROM
YOUR PRECEPTS;
THEREFORE I
HATE EVERY
WRONG PATH.
YOUR WORD IS A
LAMP TO MY FEET
AND A LIGHT FOR
MY PATH"

53

54

THE BIBLE IS A LAMP THAT LIGHTS OUR WAY IN THE DARKNESS OF SIN AND TEMPTATION.

USING THE GRID, DRAW THE PICTURE BELOW ON THE NEXT PAGE.

54

55

FROM THE PREVIOUS PAGE, USE THE GRID TO DRAW THE PICTURE FOR YOURSELF

55

56

THE SECOND ENEMY IN OUR WALK WITH THE LORD IS OUR SINFUL NATURE, ALSO KNOWN AS THE "FLESH". THIS SINFUL NATURE OR FLESH IS A PART OF ALL OF US. WE ARE BORN WITH IT.

USE THE CODE CHART BELOW TO MATCH THE CODES WITH LETTERS. USE THE COLUMN GOING DOWN, FIRST, THEN WRITE THE LETTERS IN THE BLANKS.

	1	2	3	4	5	6	7
4			Z	Y	X	W	V
3	O	P	Q	R	S	T	U
2	N	M	L	K	J	I	H
1	A	B	C	D	E	F	G

"THE ACTS OF THE
SINFUL NATURE ARE
ANGER, JEALOUSY
NOT SHARING, HATING
LYING, MAKING OTHERS
ANGRY, WORSHIPPING
FALSE GODS, AND
WITCHCRAFT"

GALATIANS 5:19-21
(CHILDREN'S BIBLE)

56

57

FIND THE WORDS BELOW IN THE WORDSEARCH PUZZLE.

WORSHIPING   ANGRY
ACTS   JEALOUSY
SINFUL   HATING
NATURE   LYING
FLESH   SHARING

57

58

THE BIBLE TELLS US HOW TO FIGHT THE DESIRES OF THE SINFUL NATURE.

USE THE CODE CHART BELOW TO MATCH THE CODES WITH LETTERS. USE THE COLUMN GOING DOWN, FIRST, THEN WRITE THE LETTERS IN THE BLANKS.

	1	2	3	4	5	6	7
			Z	Y	X	W	V
	O	P	Q	R	S	T	U
	N	M	L	K	J	I	H
	A	B	C	D	E	F	G

"THOSE WHO BELONG TO
CHRIST JESUS HAVE
CRUCIFIED THE SINFUL
NATURE WITH ITS
PASSIONS AND DESIRES.
SINCE WE LIVE BY THE
SPIRIT, LET US KEEP
IN STEP WITH THE
SPIRIT"

GALATIANS 5:24-25

58

59

FIND THE WORDS BELOW IN THE WORDSEARCH PUZZLE.

JESUS   STEP
SPIRIT   DESIRES
BELONG   KEEP
PASSIONS   CHRIST
CRUCIFIED   LIVE

59

60

MAKE YOUR WAY THROUGH THE MAZE. WATCH OUT FOR DEAD ENDS, ESPECIALLY SOME OF THE ACTS OF THE SINFUL NATURE.

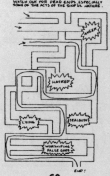

END !

60

FINISH THE FACE
YOU DO THE DRAWING! DRAW THE
EXPRESSION FOR JOY:

JOY— A FRUIT OF THE HOLY SPIRIT!

61

FINISH THE FACE
YOU DO THE DRAWING! DRAW THE
EXPRESSION FOR PEACE:

PEACE - A FRUIT OF THE HOLY SPIRIT!

62

FINISH THE FACE
YOU DO THE DRAWING! DRAW THE
EXPRESSION FOR LOVE:

LOVE - A FRUIT OF THE HOLY SPIRIT!

63

FINISH THE FACE
YOU DO THE DRAWING! DRAW THE
EXPRESSION FOR ANGER:

ANGER - AN ACT OF THE SINFUL NATURE.

64

FINISH THE FACE
YOU DO THE DRAWING! DRAW THE
EXPRESSION FOR HATRED!

HATRED - AN ACT OF THE SINFUL NATURE

65

THE THIRD ENEMY IN OUR LIVES WITH GOD
IS THE WORLD.

IT IS NOT THE WORLD IN ITSELF THAT IS
OUR ENEMY AS GOD CREATED THE WORLD.
IT IS SOME OF THE THINGS IN THE WORLD
THAT CAN LEAD US AWAY FROM GOD AND
WHAT HE WANTS US TO DO.

GO THROUGH THE MAZE.

66

CIRCLE THOSE THINGS THAT COULD BE USED
TO TEMPT YOU TO SIN AND TAKE YOU AWAY
FROM GOD'S PLAN FOR YOUR LIFE.
(YOU MAY BE SURPRISED!)

A LOT OF THINGS CAN
BE USED FOR BAD AS WELL
AS GOOD!

67

WHAT DOES GOD SAY ABOUT THE THINGS OF
THE WORLD?

USE THE CODE CHART BELOW TO MATCH
THE CODES WITH LETTERS. USE THE
COLUMN GOING DOWN, FIRST, THEN WRITE
THE LETTERS IN THE BLANKS.

	1	2	3	4	5	6	7
4			Z	Y	X	W	V
3	O	P	Q	R	S	T	U
2	N	M	L	K	J	I	H
1	A	B	C	D	E	F	G

"DO NOT LOVE THE
WORLD OR ANYTHING
IN THE WORLD. IF
ANYONE LOVES THE
WORLD, THE LOVE OF
THE FATHER IS NOT
IN HIM"

1 JOHN 2:15

68

UNSCRAMBLE THE UNDERLINED WORDS
AND PLACE THEM IN THE CORRECT SPACE
IN THE CROSSWORD GRID ON THE NEXT PAGE

ACROSS

1. THE HOLY SPIRIT WILL LEAD YOU IN
ALL TURHT.

2. YOUR YBOD IS THE TEMPLE OF THE
HOLY SPIRIT

3. YOU HAVE THREE ENEMIES. ONE OF T
IS THE IVDEL.

4. ANOTHER OF YOUR ENEMIES IS YOUR
FLESH, OR THE SINFUL AERTUN.

DOWN

5. THE HOLY SPIRIT IS ALSO CALLED
THE LORSECNUO.

6. YOU ARE TO BE CHANGED BY THE
RENEWING OF YOUR NMDI.

7. THE HOLY SPIRIT WILL PRODUCE
GOD'S TFIUR IN YOU.

8. YOUR THIRD ENEMY IS THE THINGS
OF THE RWLDO.

WORD LIST

MIND	DEVIL
BODY	NATURE
COUNSELOR	TRUTH
WORLD	FRUIT

69

70

EVEN THOUGH YOU ARE NOW GOD'S CHILD, YOU WILL STILL SIN. WHAT DO YOU DO THEN? TRAVEL THE PATH THAT MAKES A SENTENCE.

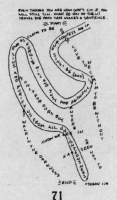

71

AFTER GOING THROUGH THE MAZE ON THE PREVIOUS PAGE, FILL IN THE BLANKS BELOW TO FINISH THE VERSE.

"IF WE **CONFESS** OUR SINS, HE (GOD) IS **FAITHFUL** AND **JUST** AND WILL **FORGIVE** US OUR **SINS** AND **PURIFY** US FROM ALL **UNRIGHTEOUSNESS**."
1 JOHN 1:9

72

FIND THE WORDS BELOW IN THE WORDSEARCH PUZZLE.

```
U F P D T P C O S P R R T I A
A L O N N F O R G I V E U T H
B L I E W A N T K N L A D K
C N E S J I F I I W S F U I
J W S E L T E E N E B E R L E
U S H S N H S P D T N U I O J
S S G E N F S O N N D C F D N
J I W S L U L I E W S G V T U
E W G E L N E S J B E L B E
U N R I G H T E O U S N E S S
S L B S N N S H S N I B H A K
S N I B H S S G E N T L E N R
E N T L E H I W S L B P P I T
```

FORGIVE   SINS

FAITHFUL   JUST

PURIFY   CONFESS

UNRIGHTEOUSNESS

73

OUR LORD JESUS PAID THE PRICE FOR OUR SINS. HE TOOK OUR PUNISHMENT BY DYING ON THE CROSS.

USING THE GRID, DRAW THE PICTURE BELOW ON THE NEXT PAGE

74

FROM THE PREVIOUS PAGE, USE THE GRID TO DRAW THE PICTURE FOR YOURSELF

75

ALL CHRISTIANS ARE TEMPTED TO SIN, TO DO THINGS THAT ARE WRONG. BUT WE CAN TRUST GOD TO HELP US IN OUR TIMES OF TEMPTATION.

USE THE CODE CHART BELOW TO MATCH THE CODES WITH LETTERS. USE THE COLUMN GOING DOWN, FIRST, THEN WRITE THE LETTERS IN THE BLANKS.

	7	6	5	4	3	2	1
1	A	H	I	P	Q	X	Y
2	B	G	J	O	R	W	Z
3	C	F	K	N	S	V	
4	D	E	L	M	T	U	

"THE ONLY TEMPTATIONS THAT YOU HAVE ARE THE TEMPTATIONS THAT ALL PEOPLE

CONT'D NEXT PAGE ...

76

CONT'D FROM PREVIOUS PAGE

HAVE. BUT YOU CAN TRUST GOD. HE WILL NOT LET YOU BE TEMPTED MORE THAN YOU CAN STAND. BUT WHEN YOU ARE, GOD WILL ALSO GIVE YOU A WAY TO ESCAPE THAT TEMPTATION. THEN YOU WILL BE ABLE TO STAND IT."
1 CORINTHIANS 10:13 (ICB/ERV BIBLE)

77

CONNECT-THE-DOTS

FIGHTING TEMPTATION ON YOUR OWN.

78

CONNECT-THE-DOTS

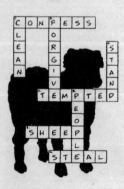

FIGHTING TEMPTATION WITH GOD!

79

SOMETIMES YOU MAY NOT FEEL LIKE YOU ARE A CHRISTIAN. YOU MAY EVEN WONDER IF JESUS REALLY DID COME INTO YOUR HEART.

USUALLY YOU FEEL LIKE THIS WHEN YOU KEEP MAKING THE SAME MISTAKE OVER AND OVER, OR WHEN IT SEEMS LIKE YOU ARE ALWAYS TEMPTED TO DO WHAT YOU KNOW IS SIN.

JESUS NEVER LIES; THE BIBLE IS TRUE. IF YOU REALLY MEANT IT WHEN YOU ASKED JESUS INTO YOUR HEART, THEN YOU CAN BELIEVE THAT JESUS IS IN YOU.

THIS IS WHAT GOD'S WORD SAYS:

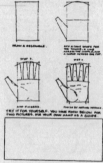

"I GIVE THEM ETERNAL LIFE,
AND THEY SHALL NEVER PERISH;
NO ONE CAN SNATCH
THEM OUT OF MY HAND."

JOHN 10:28

80

THE ONLY WAY TO HEAVEN IS THROUGH JESUS CHRIST. HAVING JESUS IN YOUR HEART MEANS YOU HAVE BEEN GIVEN ETERNAL LIFE, AND YOU WILL LIVE WITH GOD FOREVER. THIS IS GOD'S PROMISE TO YOU!

FIND THE UNDERLINED WORDS IN THE WORDSEARCH PUZZLE BELOW

"I GIVE THEM ETERNAL
LIFE, AND THEY SHALL NEVER
PERISH; NO ONE CAN SNATCH
THEM OUT OF MY HAND."

81

FROM THE START OF YOUR CHRISTIAN LIFE TO THE END OF IT, YOU WILL ALWAYS STAY IN THE HAND OF THE LORD JESUS.

LIFE WILL NOT ALWAYS BE EASY, BUT JESUS WILL GET YOU THROUGH!

FIND YOUR WAY THROUGH THE MAZE OF LIFE.

START

END

82

HOW TO DRAW THE HAND

STEP 1.   STEP 2.

DRAW A RECTANGLE.   ADD A LONG SHAPE FOR THE THUMB. ALSO A SMALLER ONE INSIDE OF THE HAND. A CURVE ACROSS THE TOP.

STEP 3.   STEP 4.

ADD FINGERS.   FINISH BY ADDING DETAILS.

TRY IT FOR YOURSELF. YOU HAVE ROOM BELOW FOR TWO PICTURES. USE YOUR OWN HAND AS A GUIDE.

83

UNSCRAMBLE THE UNDERLINED WORDS AND PLACE THEM IN THE CROSSWORD GRID ON THE NEXT PAGE.

ACROSS

1. WE ARE TO SSFCNOE OUR SINS TO GOD.

2. WE ARE ALL PTMTDEE TO SIN.

3. THE BIBLE SAYS THAT PEOPLE ARE LIKE PHESE.

4. NO ONE CAN ASETL US OUT OF GOD'S HAND.

DOWN

1. GOD WILL MAKE OUR HEARTS CLNAE AND NEW.

2. GOD WILL EFGRVOI US FOR OUR SINS.

3. THE TEMPTATIONS THAT COME ARE WHAT COME TO ALL EEPOLP.

4. GOD WILL GIVE US A WAY TO ESCAPE TEMPTATION SO WE CAN ASDNT.

WORD LIST

SHEEP   PEOPLE
STAND   FORGIVE
CONFESS   STEAL
TEMPTED   CLEAN

84

85

IF YOU REMEMBER, WHEN YOU INVITE JESUS CHRIST INTO YOUR LIFE, YOUR BODY BECOMES THE TEMPLE OF GOD'S HOLY SPIRIT

IN OTHER WORDS, YOUR BODY BECOMES THE "HOUSE" THAT THE HOLY SPIRIT DWELLS IN. AS YOU LIVE IN A HOUSE THAT NEEDS CLEANING, SO DOES YOUR "BODY-HOUSE" NEED CLEANING. THE HOLY SPIRIT WANTS TO CLEAN UP WRONG THINKING AND ACTIONS.

THE HOUSE WITHOUT JESUS:

COLOR THE PICTURE.

86

NOW THAT THE HOLY SPIRIT LIVES IN YOU, HE IS GOING TO WANT TO CLEAN AND EVEN CHANGE SOME THINGS IN HIS HOUSE!

THIS TAKES TIME, BUT THE RESULT IS THAT YOU ARE MADE FREE AND MUCH HAPPIER. AND JUST LIKE A NICE CLEAN HOUSE, YOU ARE MORE INVITING TO OTHERS. PEOPLE WILL WANT TO BE AROUND YOU, AND YOU CAN SHARE WITH THEM WHAT JESUS HAS DONE IN YOUR LIFE!

THE HOUSE WITH JESUS:

COLOR THE PICTURE.

87

Panel 88

SO THROUGH THE HOUSE BELOW AND PICK UP THOSE THINGS THAT GOD WOULD CLEAN OUT. WRITE THEM IN THE BLANK SPACES BELOW.

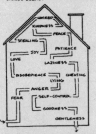

FEAR	STEALING
ANGER	HATRED
LYING	LAZINESS
DISOBEDIENCE	CHEATING

88

Panel 89

AGAIN, IT IS THE WORK OF THE HOLY SPIRIT THAT DOES THE CLEANING IN US. HE ONLY NEEDS US TO BE WILLING TO LET HIM DO THAT WORK.

GOD'S WORD GIVES US A PROMISE!

FIND THE UNDERLINED WORDS IN THE WORDSEARCH PUZZLE BELOW.

"BE CONFIDENT OF THIS, THAT HE WHO BEGAN A GOOD WORK IN YOU WILL CARRY IT ON TO THE FINISH UNTIL JESUS CHRIST COMES AGAIN."

PHILIPPIANS 1:6
(CHILDREN'S BIBLE)

```
P Q G T N F B Y N N D G Y D
T S W S C U L E E W S R A T
I W O R K H E R G V R N A C
F A E H I W S L B X I N G
I L E F N E G L C A N I M H
N Q G T G F T V N N A W C P
I L L C O N F I D E N T P I
S L N H O J B L S B G H F S
H P E R O S H J E S U S W T
E L N E B J B X Y B Z T L D
```

89

Panel 90

PICTURE YOURSELF AS A SOLDIER! YOU ARE NOW A SOLDIER FOR JESUS CHRIST, AND HE GIVES US EVERYTHING WE NEED TO WIN THE BATTLE.

USE THE CODE CHART BELOW TO MATCH THE CODES WITH LETTERS. USE THE COLUMN GOING DOWN FIRST, THEN WRITE THE LETTERS IN THE BLANKS.

	1	2	3	4	5	6
5	A	F	K	P	U	Z
4	B	G	L	Q	V	
3	C	H	M	R	W	
2	D	I	N	S	X	
1	E	J	O	T	Y	

FINALLY, BE
STRONG IN THE
LORD AND IN HIS
MIGHTY POWER.

CONT'D NEXT PAGE...

90

Panel 91

CONT'D FROM PREVIOUS PAGE.

PUT ON THE FULL
ARMOR OF GOD
SO THAT YOU CAN
TAKE YOUR STAND
AGAINST THE
DEVIL'S SCHEMES."

EPHESIANS 6:10-11

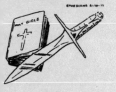

91

Panel 92

FIND THE UNDERLINED WORDS IN THE WORDSEARCH PUZZLE BELOW.

" STAND FIRM THEN, WITH THE BELT OF TRUTH BUCKLED AROUND YOUR WAIST, WITH THE BREAST PLATE OF RIGHTEOUSNESS IN PLACE, AND WITH YOUR FEET FITTED WITH THE READINESS THAT COMES FROM THE GOSPEL OF PEACE. IN ADDITION TO ALL THIS, TAKE UP THE SHIELD OF FAITH WITH WHICH YOU CAN EXTINGUISH ALL THE FLAMING ARROWS OF THE EVIL ONE. TAKE THE HELMET OF SALVATION AND THE SWORD OF THE SPIRIT, WHICH IS THE WORD OF GOD."

EPHESIANS 6:14-17

THIS IS THE FULL ARMOR OF GOD!

```
I U L C H N F G O S P E L
S L B R E A S T P L A T E D
H P E R L S H N H E S U V N N
E L N E M J B T X L L D
W Q G T E B V N E X C V T
O S F I T T E D X L W P U R
R W B R K H E R G L R O A U
O A E H I W S L B D P T M T
I L S A L V A T I O N I M H
S W O R D F T V N N A W C R
```

SHIELD	FITTED
WORD	TRUTH
HELMET	SWORD
BELT	GOSPEL
SALVATION	BREASTPLATE

92

Panel 93

FILL IN THE BLANKS.

SWORD OF THE
SPIRIT

HELMET OF
SALVATION

SHOES OF
THE GOSPEL

BELT OF TRUTH

BREASTPLATE
OF
RIGHTEOUSNESS

SHIELD OF
FAITH

THE FULL ARMOR OF GOD!

93

Panel 94

FINISH THE PICTURE.

DRAW OVER THE DOTTED LINES TO "DRESS" IN THE ARMOR OF GOD.

94

Panel 95

FIND YOUR WAY THROUGH THE BATTLEFIELD OF LIFE. WATCH OUT FOR TEMPTATION AND SIN!

END

95

Panel 96

DO YOU REMEMBER OUR THREE ENEMIES THE WORLD, THE FLESH (OR SINFUL NATURE), AND THE DEVIL?

WE CALL THE BATTLE AGAINST THESE ENEMIES SPIRITUAL WARFARE.

GOD'S WORD HAS SOMETHING TO SAY ABOUT THIS WARFARE.

" FOR OUR STRUGGLE (OUR BATTLE) IS NOT AGAINST FLESH AND BLOOD, BUT AGAINST THE RULERS, AGAINST THE AUTHORITIES, AGAINST THE POWERS OF THIS DARK WORLD AND AGAINST THE SPIRITUAL FORCES OF EVIL IN THE HEAVENLY REALMS (THE UNSEEN SPIRITUAL WORLD AROUND US)."

EPHESIANS 6:12

96

FIND THE WORDS BELOW IN THE
WORD SEARCH.

FLESH   RULERS
EVIL   BLOOD
WORLD   HEAVENLY
STRUGGLE   AUTHORITIES

NOW IT IS TIME TO START LIVING YOUR
LIFE AS A CHILD OF GOD.

THERE ARE MANY THINGS IN LIFE THAT
CAN DISTRACT US, OR LEAD US AWAY,
FROM JESUS.

WHAT DOES JESUS SAY WE SHOULD DO?

UNSCRAMBLE THE WORDS AND PUT
THEM IN THE RIGHT PLACES IN THE
VERSE BELOW.

" LET US X.F.I OUR EYES ON JESUS,
THE A.OTUHO AND PERFECTER OF
OUR A.F.H.T, WHO FOR THE O.Y SET
E.B.R.F.EO HIM ENDURED THE C.O.S.S,
SCORNING ITS M.H.SEA, AND SAT
N.OPN AT THE RIGHT N.D.HA OF THE
H.T.N.R.O.E OF GOD."

                        HEBREWS 12:2

" LET US FIX OUR EYES ON
JESUS , THE AUTHOR AND
PERFECTER OF OUR FAITH ,
WHO FOR THE JOY SET BEFORE
HIM ENDURED THE CROSS ,
SCORNING ITS SHAME , AND SAT
DOWN AT THE RIGHT HAND OF
THE THRONE OF GOD."

You're in for the ultimate

American Adventure!

Collect all 48 books!